OCR
Revise
Chemistry

AS

Exclusively endorsed by OCR for GCE Chemistry A

Second Edition

Mike Wooster and Helen Eccles
Series editor: Rob Ritchie

www.heinemann.co.uk

✓ Free online support
✓ Useful weblinks
✓ 24 hour online ordering

01865 888080

In Exclusive Partnership

Heinemann is an imprint of Pearson Education Limited, a company incorporated in England and Wales, having its registered office at Edinburgh Gate, Harlow, Essex, CM20 2JE. Registered company number: 872828

www.heinemann.co.uk

Heinemann is a registered trademark of Pearson Education Limited

Text © Mike Wooster, Helen Eccles, 2008

First published 2000
This edition 2008

12 11 10 09 08
10 9 8 7 6 5 4 3 2

British Library Cataloguing in Publication Data is available from the British Library on request.

ISBN 978 0 435583 71 2

Edited by Anne Sweetmore
Designed by Wearset Ltd, Boldon, Tyne and Wear
Project managed and typeset by Wearset Ltd, Boldon, Tyne and Wear
Original illustrations © Pearson Education Limited 2008
Illustrated by Wearset Ltd, Boldon, Tyne and Wear
Cover design by Wearset Ltd, Boldon, Tyne and Wear
Cover photo of calcium phosphate crystals © Science Photo Library
Printed in the UK by Ashford Colour Press Ltd

Every effort has been made to contact copyright holders of material reproduced in this book. Any omissions will be rectified in subsequent printings if notice is given to the publishers.

Contents

Introduction

How to use this revision guide

This revision guide is for the OCR Chemistry AS course.

In the AS year you will complete two written units. This means that you will take two written exams called 'Atoms, bonds and groups' and 'Chains, energy and resources'. Each of the two units is conveniently broken up into modules and these are listed on the page of contents. There is no synoptic element to the AS year of study – this means each unit is self-contained. However, the material in the first unit (Atoms, bonds and groups) is the basis for the other unit and for units in the A2 exam as well, so you can't forget it just because you've taken the exam.

If you are going on to study Chemistry at A2 (Advanced) level, the basic organisation is the same.

Remember to revisit each module more than once. This will increase your recall of the facts and the quality of your understanding.

At the end of each double-page spread you will see 'Quick check questions'. These will test your understanding of the basic facts for that section. The answers to these short questions are at the end of the book so you check how well you are doing. There are also 'End-of-unit questions' that are more like exam questions and you can use these when you are near the end of your revision.

OCR AS Chemistry

What will you study to get this qualification?

In the AS year you will complete three units, one of which is a practical unit. This means that you will take two written exams: 'Atoms, Bonds and Groups' and 'Chains, Energy and Resources'. There is no synoptic element to the AS year of study – each unit is self-contained. However, the material in the Atoms, Bonds and Groups unit is the basis for the other units, so you will need to remember it.

In the Chains, Energy and Resources unit, there is a 'Background Facts' section for the main groups of compounds, which gives you an overview of the main concepts and facts. This will point you to the important areas in the section, and give you a useful page for comparison between organic families of compounds for your revision. This is particularly important in the 'Chains and Rings' module, because many students find sorting out the differences between organic compounds confusing.

If you are interested in studying chemistry at A2 level, you will find that the OCR A2 course consists of a further three units.

Good luck with your revision!

Significant figures in calculations

Sig. figs, as they are known, can be important in chemical calculations. How do you work out the number of sig. figs in a number? The general rule is that *all digits are significant, except zeros that are used to position the decimal point*. Here are some rules to help you apply this generalisation.

- All **non-zero digits** are significant. So 45.9 has three sig. figs; 18.224 has five sig. figs.
- **Zeros between sig. figs** are significant. So 601.4 has four sig. figs; 100.05 has five sig. figs.
- **Zeros to the left** of the first non-zero digit are **not** significant. So 0.074 has two sig. figs; 0.0201 has three sig. figs.
- A **zero that ends a number** and is to the right of the decimal point is significant. So 43.790 has five sig. figs; 3.020 has four sig. figs.
- **Exponentials** are used to indicate the number of sig. figs where a zero ends the number and is to the left of the decimal point. So 5.300×10^3 has four sig. figs; 5.3×10^3 has two sig. figs.

To work out how many sig. figs you should use in your answer, look at the figures given in the question. You should use the same number of sig. figs in your answer as the *lowest* number of sig. figs given in the question. When you are doing the calculation, use one or two more sig. figs than this, and then round off your final answer to the correct number of sig. figs.

UNIT 1 (F321)

Atoms, bonds and groups

This is the first unit of the AS and A2 course, and it is important for two reasons: it contains all the material needed to understand the other units; and topics covered in this unit crop up in questions for the other units.

You will find that some of the material in this unit is familiar to you from your GCSE course. This is because the Atoms, bonds and groups unit is a bridge into AS chemistry from GCSE science/chemistry. So, although this unit looks large, don't worry – you know some of it already!

Module 1 – Atoms and reactions, pages 2–17

Topic (in this book)	Reference to specification	Ideas from GCSE
Atoms, molecules and stoichiometry	1.1.1	GCSE material on atomic structure and atomic mass. Constructing and balancing symbol equations.
Isotopes and relative masses	1.1.1	Atomic structure and atomic mass.
Amount of substance – the mole	1.1.2	Numerical aspects of the GCSE course.
Types of mole calculation	1.1.2	You may have done this at GCSE level. Take account of the notes on significant figures.
Empirical and molecular formulae	1.1.2	You will refer to the moles section continually here.
Acids, bases and salts	1.1.3	Previous work on these types of compounds – revise balancing of equations.
Water of crystallisation and titration calculations	1.1.2 and 1.1.3	Again, you must be able to do mole calculations.
Oxidation and reduction	1.1.4	Remember the definitions you learned at GCSE.

Module 2 – Electrons, bonding and structure, pages 18–29

Topic (in this book)	Reference to specification	Ideas from GCSE
Ionisation energy	1.2.1	Electron arrangements.
Electron configurations – the arrangement of electrons in an atom	1.2.1	GCSE material on the arrangement of electrons in shells.
Chemical bonding	1.2.2	Electron arrangements and ionic and covalent bonding, dot-and-cross diagrams. How atoms become ions.
Shapes of molecules – electron pair repulsion theory	1.2.2	The tetrahedral structure of methane from GCSE.
Electronegativity, polarity and intermolecular forces	1.2.2	You may have done some work at GCSE on van der Waals' forces.
Structures and physical properties	1.2.2	Your knowledge of the physical properties of ionic and covalent compounds from GCSE.

Module 3 – The Periodic Table, pages 30–39

Topic (in this book)	Reference to specification	Ideas from GCSE
The Periodic Table	1.3.1	GCSE work on the structure of the Periodic Table and the locations of groups and periods.
The Periodic Table and periodicity in the elements of Periods 2 and 3	1.3.1	GCSE work on the structure of the Periodic Table and the locations of groups and periods.
The Group 2 elements	1.3.2	Knowledge of magnesium, calcium and their compounds.
The Group 7 elements	1.3.3	Knowledge of chlorine, bromine and their compounds. Use your knowledge of oxidation numbers from previous modules in the unit.

End-of-unit questions, pages 40–41

UNIT 1

Atoms, molecules and stoichiometry

Quick revision checklist

Make sure you know:

- The relative masses and charges of the proton, neutron and electron.
- Atoms are neutral; positive ions (cations) have lost electrons; negative ions (anions) have gained electrons. The number of charges on the ion is the number of electrons gained or lost by the atom.
- **Atomic number** Z = number of protons = number of electrons. This is also the position of the element in the Periodic Table, so for instance element 20 (calcium) has 20 electrons and 20 protons.
- **Mass number** A = number of protons + number of neutrons. So $A - Z$ = number of neutrons.
- The atomic mass A and atomic number Z are shown as superscripts and subscripts next to the symbol for the element.

✓*Quick check 1 and 2*

■ WORKED EXAMPLE

How many protons, neutrons and electrons are there in an atom of phosphorus, $^{31}_{15}P$?

STEP 1 The subscript is 15, therefore the atomic number, Z, is 15. This means there are 15 protons and 15 electrons.

STEP 2 The superscript is 31, therefore the mass number is 31. This means the number of neutrons = $A - Z$ = 31 − 15 = 16.

Working out formulae using ions

- The formula of an ionic compound can be worked out using the charges on the ions.
- The charges have to cancel each other out.
- Therefore for two ions, A^{m+} and B^{n-}, the formula of the compound will be A_nB_m.
- Remember, if the ion is polyatomic, e.g. SO_4^{2-}, then you put brackets around it if more than one is present in the formula, e.g. $Al_2(SO_4)_3$.

✓*Quick check 3*

Symbol equations

Symbol equations are important in chemistry because they tell us in what proportions substances react together. Equations have to be balanced – they must have the same number of atoms on each side of the arrow. Balance an equation by putting numbers *in front of the formulae only*.

■ WORKED EXAMPLE

Balance this equation: $H_2S + O_2 \rightarrow H_2O + SO_2$

STEP 1 Don't change any of the formulae, just put numbers in front of the formulae until there are the same numbers of atoms on each side of the arrow.

✓*Quick check 4*

STEP 2 This gives $2H_2S + 3O_2 \rightarrow 2H_2O + 2SO_2$

✓*Quick check 6*

Constructing equations

Equations can also be constructed. This means that if the reactants and products of a reaction are known, then the balanced chemical equation can be written down.

■ WORKED EXAMPLE

Sodium reacts with oxygen to give sodium oxide.

STEP 1 Think of the word equation: sodium + oxygen → sodium oxide.

STEP 2 Write down the symbols for the reactants and products: $Na + O_2 \rightarrow Na_2O$.

STEP 3 Balance the equation: $4Na(s) + O_2(g) \rightarrow 2Na_2O(s)$.

Ionic equations

Equations can be **ionic**. Ionic equations show just the ions that take part in the reaction.

■ WORKED EXAMPLE

Write down the ionic equation for: $NaOH(aq) + HCl(aq) \rightarrow NaCl(aq) + H_2O(l)$

STEP 1 Split each ionic compound up into its ions. Leave the **covalent** molecules as they are.

$$Na^+(aq) + OH^-(aq) + H^+(aq) + Cl^-(aq) \rightarrow Na^+(aq) + Cl^-(aq) + H_2O(l)$$

STEP 2 Cross out any ions that appear on each side of the arrow (check you are crossing out the same number of each type of ion):

$$\cancel{Na^+(aq)} + OH^-(aq) + H^+(aq) + \cancel{Cl^-(aq)} \rightarrow \cancel{Na^+(aq)} + \cancel{Cl^-(aq)} + H_2O(l)$$

STEP 3 This leaves the ionic equation: $OH^-(aq) + H^+(aq) \rightarrow H_2O(l)$.

✔ *Quick check 5 and 6*

Cations	
Sodium	Na^+
Lithium	Li^+
Potassium	K^+
Ammonium	NH_4^+
Magnesium	Mg^{2+}
Calcium	Ca^{2+}
Barium	Ba^{2+}
Silver	Ag^+
Iron(II)	Fe^{2+}
Iron(III)	Fe^{3+}
Lead	Pb^{2+}
Copper(II)	Cu^{2+}

Anions	
Hydroxide	OH^-
Nitrate	NO_3^-
Fluoride	F^-
Chloride	Cl^-
Bromide	Br^-
Iodide	I^-
Sulfate	SO_4^{2-}
Sulfite	SO_3^{2-}
Oxide	O^{2-}
Carbonate	CO_3^{2-}
Sulfide	S^{2-}
Phosphate	PO_4^{3-}

Module 1

QUICK CHECK QUESTIONS

1. How many protons, neutrons and electrons are there in
   a $^{40}_{20}Ca$
   b $^{16}_{8}O$
   c $^{14}_{6}C$?

2. How many electrons are there in
   a $^{19}_{9}F^-$
   b $^{27}_{13}Al^{3+}$
   c $^{24}_{12}Mg^{2+}$?

3. Write down the formulae of:
   a calcium hydroxide
   b lead phosphate
   c barium carbonate
   d potassium sulfate
   e iron(III) hydroxide.

4. Balance these equations:
   a $N_2 + H_2 \rightarrow NH_3$
   b $Fe + H_2O \rightarrow Fe_3O_4 + H_2$
   c $Na_2O + H_2O \rightarrow NaOH$
   d $PCl_5 + H_2O \rightarrow H_3PO_4 + HCl$

5. Write the ionic equations for the following reactions
   a $2KBr(aq) + Cl_2(g) \rightarrow 2KCl(aq) + Br_2(aq)$
   b $Mg(s) + 2HCl(aq) \rightarrow MgCl_2(aq) + H_2(g)$

6. a Construct a symbol equation showing the reaction between sulfuric acid and magnesium that gives magnesium sulfate and hydrogen as the products.
   b Give the ionic equation for this reaction.

UNIT 1

Isotopes and relative masses

Module 1

Key words

- relative formula mass
- relative atomic mass
- relative isotopic mass
- relative abundance

✓ *Quick check 1*

✓ *Quick check 2*

Hint

^{12}C is the standard used, and 1/12 the mass of ^{12}C is 1.

Hint

Weighted mean mass takes into account the relative abundance of each isotope.

✓ *Quick check 3*

Isotopes

- Different **isotopes** of the same element have the same number of protons and electrons, but different numbers of neutrons.

■ WORKED EXAMPLE

Chlorine has two naturally occurring isotopes, $^{35}_{17}Cl$ and $^{37}_{17}Cl$. Both isotopes have 17 protons and 17 electrons, but $^{35}_{17}C$ has 18 neutrons and $^{37}_{17}Cl$ has 20 neutrons.

Relative isotopic mass

- The relative isotopic mass is the mass of an atom of an isotope of an element relative to one-twelfth (1/12) the mass of ^{12}C.

For example, the relative isotopic mass of $^{35}_{17}Cl$ is 35.

Relative atomic mass

- The relative atomic mass (A_r) of an element is the weighted mean mass of an atom of an element, relative to 1/12 the mass of ^{12}C.

The following worked example shows how to calculate the relative atomic mass, A_r, from the relative abundances of the isotopes.

■ WORKED EXAMPLE

The relative isotopic masses and relative abundances of the three naturally occurring isotopes of an element are shown in the table below:

Relative isotopic mass	Relative abundance
54	6
56	92
57	2

STEP 1 Let there be 100 atoms. The number of atoms of each isotope is the percentage relative abundance.

STEP 2 Multiply each relative isotopic mass by the percentage relative abundance to give the total mass of each isotope:

$6 \times 54 = 324$

$92 \times 56 = 5152$

$2 \times 57 = 114$

STEP 3 If we add all these together, we get the mass of 100 atoms:

$324 + 5152 + 114 = 5590$

STEP 4 To get the weighted mean mass, we divide by 100.

Relative atomic mass $(A_r) = \dfrac{5590}{100} = 55.90$ (no units)

Relative molecular mass and relative formula mass

You do not have to define these terms, but it is very important that you know how to work them out.

- **Relative molecular mass M_r** refers to the relative mass of a molecule of a compound.
- **Relative formula mass** refers to the relative mass of a compound with a giant structure, such as NaCl (giant ionic) or SiO_2 (giant covalent).
- The relative molecular mass of a molecule is calculated by adding together the relative atomic masses of all the atoms *in the molecule*.
- The relative formula mass of an ionic or giant covalent compound is calculated by adding together the relative atomic masses of all the atoms *in the formula*.

■ WORKED EXAMPLE

What is the relative formula mass of $(NH_4)_2SO_4$?

STEP 1 Take account of the brackets. In this example, there are brackets around the NH_4^+ ion. Therefore there are two of whatever is inside the bracket.

STEP 2 Count up the atoms of each element in the formula. In this formula there are 2 nitrogens, 8 hydrogens, 1 sulfur and 4 oxygens.

STEP 3 Add up the relative atomic masses (see page 31) of all the atoms in the molecule.

$$(2 \times 14.0) + (8 \times 1.0) + (1 \times 32.1) + (4 \times 16.0) = 28.0 + 8.0 + 32.1 + 64.0 = 132.1$$

The relative formula mass of $(NH_4)_2SO_4 = \mathbf{132.1}$ (no units)

✓*Quick check 4*

QUICK CHECK QUESTIONS

1. **a** How do the following isotopes resemble each other?
   - **i** $^{56}_{26}Fe$ and $^{57}_{26}Fe$ **ii** $^{78}_{36}Kr$ and $^{80}_{36}Kr$
   b Explain how these isotopes differ.

2. What are the relative isotopic masses of the following?
   - **a** $^{40}_{18}Ar$ **b** $^{50}_{24}Cr$
   - **c** $^{65}_{29}Cu$

3. There are two isotopes of boron. Their relative isotopic masses and their relative abundances are given in the table below. Use the data to calculate the relative atomic mass of boron.

Relative isotopic mass	Relative abundance (%)
10	19.7
11	80.3

4. Calculate the relative formula mass of the following:
   - **a** $MgCl_2$ **b** $CaCO_3$
   - **c** $(NH_4)_3PO_4$ **d** $Cu(NO_3)_2$
   - **e** $Al_2(SO_4)_3$

UNIT 1

Amount of substance – the mole

Equations tell us the proportions in which substances react together. We need to be able to convert those amounts into grams, so we use the **mole**, which is the unit for **amount of substance**. A mole of any one substance has the *same number of particles* as a mole of another substance. Because atoms of different substances have different masses, a mole of any one substance has a *different mass* from a mole of another substance.

A mole (1 mol) of a substance is the amount of substance that contains 6.02×10^{23} particles, which is the same number of particles as there are atoms in exactly 12 g of ^{12}C.

The number 6.02×10^{23} is called the **Avogadro constant**, symbol N_A, units mol^{-1}.

Chemists often work out the mass in g of 1 mol of substance – this is called the **molar mass**.

Molar mass

The molar mass is the mass per mole of the substance in g. It has the symbol M and units $g\,mol^{-1}$.

> ### ■ WORKED EXAMPLE
>
> Find the molar mass of sulfuric acid, H_2SO_4. Relative atomic masses (H) = 1.0; S = 32.1; O = 16.0.
>
> Work this out exactly as for a relative formula mass, but include units.
>
> **STEP 1** Add up the relative masses of all the atoms:
>
> $$(1.00 \times 2) + 32.1 + (16.0 \times 4) = 98.1$$
>
> **STEP 2** Add the units: **$98.1\,g\,mol^{-1}$**.

> ### ■ WORKED EXAMPLE
>
> Find the molar mass of lithium bromide.
>
> **STEP 1** Write down the formula of lithium bromide: **LiBr**.
>
> **STEP 2** Add up the relative masses of all the atoms: **Li = 6.9; Br = 79.9**.
>
> $$6.9 + 79.9 = 86.8$$
>
> **STEP 3** Add the units: **$86.8\,g\,mol^{-1}$**.

Mole calculations

There are three main types of equation involving the mole: for solids, solutions and gases.

For solids:

For both elements and compounds	Can be rearranged
Amount (mol) = $\dfrac{\text{mass (g)}}{\text{molar mass } M}$	Mass (g) = amount (mol molar mass) × molar mass M

■ WORKED EXAMPLE

How many moles are there in 5.00 g of calcium nitrate, $Ca(NO_3)_2$?

STEP 1 Work out the molar mass of calcium nitrate, $Ca(NO_3)_2$:

$$M = 40.1 + (14.0 \times 2) + (16.0 \times 6) = 164.1$$

STEP 2 Apply the equation: $\text{amount (mol)} = \dfrac{\text{mass (g)}}{M} = \dfrac{5.00}{164.1} = 0.0305 \text{ mol}$

✓ *Quick check 3*

For solutions:

	Can be rearranged
Amount (mol) = volume (dm^3) × concentration (mol dm^{-3})	Concentration (mol dm^{-3}) = $\dfrac{\text{amount (mol)}}{\text{volume (dm}^3\text{)}}$
or	
Amount (mol) = [volume (cm^3)/1000] × concentration (mol dm^{-3})	Concentration (mol dm^{-3}) = $\dfrac{\text{amount (mol)}}{\text{volume (cm}^3\text{)} \times 10^{-3}}$

✓ *Quick check 4*

■ WORKED EXAMPLE

How many moles of sodium hydroxide are there in 10 cm^3 of 0.100 mol dm^{-3} aqueous sodium hydroxide?

STEP 1 Apply the equation:

$$\text{amount (mol)} = \frac{\text{vol (cm}^3\text{)}}{1000} \times \text{concentration} = \frac{10}{1000} \times 0.100 = 0.0010 \text{ mol}$$

For gases:

	Can be rearranged
Amount of gas (mol) = $\dfrac{\text{volume (dm}^3\text{)}}{24}$ at RTP	Volume (dm^3) = amount of gas (mol) × 24
or	
Amount of gas (mol) = $\dfrac{\text{volume (cm}^3\text{)}}{24\,000}$ at RTP	Volume (cm^3) = amount of gas (mol) × 24 000

Hint

1 mole of gas occupies 24 dm^3 at room temperature and pressure (RTP).

✓ *Quick check 5*

■ WORKED EXAMPLE

How many moles of oxygen occupy 600 cm^3 at room temperature and pressure?

STEP 1 Apply the equation:

$$\text{amount of gas (mol)} = \frac{\text{vol (cm}^3\text{)}}{24\,000} = \frac{600}{24\,000} = 0.0250 \text{ mol}$$

QUICK CHECK QUESTIONS

1. How many atoms are there in the following?
   a. 2.00 mol of Si atoms.
   b. 2.00 mol of CH_4 molecules.
2. What is the molar mass of NaI?
3. How many moles of $CaCO_3$ are there in 2.00 g of the solid?

4. How many moles of H_2SO_4 are there in 25.0 cm^3 of a 0.200 mol dm^{-3} solution?
5. a. What is the volume of 0.200 mol of NH_3 gas at room temperature and pressure?
   b. How many moles of HCl gas are there in 1440 cm^3 of the gas at room temperature and pressure?

Types of mole calculation

Calculating mass

Mass (of a solid) from the amount in mol

■ **WORKED EXAMPLE**

What is the mass of 2 moles of calcium sulfate, $CaSO_4$?

STEP 1 Calculate the molar mass, M, of $CaSO_4$: $M = 40.1 + 32.1 + (16.0 \times 4) = 136.2$

STEP 2 Use the rearranged mole equation for solids:

Mass (g) = amount (mol) $\times M = 2 \times 136.2 = 272.4\,g$

Mass (of a solid) from an equation

✓*Quick check 1*

■ **WORKED EXAMPLE**

What mass of calcium carbonate reacts completely with $25.0\,cm^3$ of $2.00\,mol\,dm^{-3}$ hydrochloric acid?

STEP 1 Construct the equation:

$$CaCO_3(s) + 2HCl(aq) \rightarrow CaCl_2(aq) + CO_2(g) + H_2O(l)$$

STEP 2 Calculate the amount, in mol, of hydrochloric acid used in the reaction:

$$\text{Amount of HCl (mol)} = \frac{\text{vol (cm}^3)}{1000} \times \text{concentration} = \frac{25}{1000} \times 2 = 0.0500\,mol$$

STEP 3 From the equation, see how many moles of calcium carbonate are needed.
1 mol calcium carbonate requires 2 mol hydrochloric acid.
1 mol HCl requires 0.5 mol calcium carbonate.
0.0500 mol HCl requires $0.0500/2\,mol = 0.0250\,mol\ CaCO_3$

STEP 4 Now use the mole equation to find the mass of calcium carbonate:

mass of $CaCO_3$ = amount (mol) $\times M = 0.025 \times [40.1 + 12.0 + (16.0 \times 3)] = 2.50\,g$

Using an equation to find the mass of product formed

■ **WORKED EXAMPLE**

What is the mass of zinc sulfate produced when 3.25 g of zinc is reacted with excess sulfuric acid?

STEP 1 Construct the equation for the reaction:

$$Zn(s) + H_2SO_4(aq) \rightarrow ZnSO_4(aq) + H_2(g)$$

STEP 2 Calculate amount in mol of zinc used:

Amount in mol of zinc = mass in g/M = $3.25/65.4 = 0.0500\,mol$

✓*Quick check 2*

STEP 3 Look at the equation to see the amount, in mol, of zinc sulfate formed:

0.0500 moles of Zn gives 0.0500 mol of $ZnSO_4$

STEP 4 Calculate the mass of $ZnSO_4$:

mass of $ZnSO_4$ = amount (in mol) $\times M = 0.0500 \times [65.4 + 32.1 + (16.0 \times 4)] = 8.08\,g$

Calculating the volume of a gas

■ WORKED EXAMPLE

In the worked example above, what volume of hydrogen (in cm^3) is produced at RTP?

STEP 1 The amount of zinc used (in mol) is already known: 0.0500 mol.

STEP 2 Look at the equation to find the amount of hydrogen produced (in mol):
0.0500 mol Zn gives 0.0500 mol H_2

STEP 3 Find the volume from the amount (in mol):
Volume (cm^3) = amount (mol) × 24 000 = 0.0500 × 24 000 = 1200 cm^3

Hint

1 mole of gas occupies 24.0 dm^3 at room temperature and pressure (RTP).

✓*Quick check 3*

Calculating the concentration of a solution

■ WORKED EXAMPLE

Calculate the concentration of 1.40 g of potassium hydroxide in 500 cm^3 of solution.

STEP 1 Calculate the amount of solid KOH used (in mol):

$$\text{Amount (mol)} = \frac{\text{mass (g)}}{M} = \frac{1.40}{56.1} = 0.0250 \text{ mol KOH}$$

STEP 2 Now find the concentration of the KOH solution:

$$\text{Concentration} = \frac{\text{amount (mol)}}{\text{volume } (cm^3 \times 10^{-3})} = \frac{0.0250}{500 \times 10^{-3}} = 0.0500 \text{ mol dm}^{-3}$$

Examiner tip

The greater the number of moles of solute dissolved in a certain volume of solvent, the more **concentrated** the solution. If the number of moles of solute dissolved in a volume of solvent is decreased, the solution becomes more **dilute**.

Equations from mole calculations

✓*Quick check 4*

■ WORKED EXAMPLE

0.10 mol magnesium reacts with 0.20 mol hydrochloric acid to give 0.10 mol magnesium chloride and 0.10 mol hydrogen. Write the equation for the reaction.

Substance	Magnesium +	hydrochloric acid →	magnesium chloride +	hydrogen
Number of mol	0.10	0.20	0.10	0.10
Whole number ratio	1	2	1	1
Equation	$Mg + 2HCl \rightarrow MgCl_2 + H_2$			

QUICK CHECK QUESTIONS

1 Calcium oxide and nitric acid react together as shown:
$CaO + 2HNO_3 \rightarrow Ca(NO_3)_2 + 2H_2O$
What is the mass of calcium oxide (CaO) that will react with 50.0 cm^3 of 1.00 mol dm^{-3} nitric acid?

2 How many moles of Ag are produced in the decomposition of 20.0 g of silver oxide?
$2Ag_2O(s) \rightarrow 4Ag(s) + O_2(g)$

3 Copper(II) oxide reacts with carbon as follows:
$2CuO + C \rightarrow CO_2 + 2Cu$
What volume of CO_2 is formed at room temperature and pressure when 7.95 g of copper oxide are heated with excess carbon?

4 A student measured the amount of ammonia produced in the following reaction:
$Ca(OH)_2(s) + 2NH_4Cl(s) \rightarrow CaCl_2(s) + 2NH_3(g) + 2H_2O(g)$
The ammonia had a volume of 600 cm^3 at room temperature and pressure.
a How many moles of ammonia were formed?
b What mass of ammonium chloride was used in the experiment?
c What was the mass of calcium chloride formed? Give your answer to two decimal places.
d If the ammonia formed was dissolved in water to form 500 cm^3 of solution, what is the concentration of this solution?

UNIT 1

Empirical and molecular formulae

Key words

- empirical formula
- molecular formula

The **empirical formula** of a compound is the *simplest whole-number ratio* of atoms of each element present in a compound – the simplest mole ratio.

The **molecular formula** is the *number of atoms* of each element in a molecule.

Empirical formula

Empirical formulae are calculated from the masses of the elements in a compound – from the masses of elements that combine with each other.

■ WORKED EXAMPLE

Calculate the empirical formula of silicon oxide if 3.50 g of silicon combines with 4.00 g of oxygen.

STEP 1 Write down the mass of each element.

STEP 2 Calculate the amount, in mol of each element in the table (divide mass by M).

STEP 3 Divide the amount in mol of each element by the smallest number that goes into both. This is the empirical formula.

(If this is not obvious, divide by the smallest amount in mol – this automatically gives a ratio of 1 for one element – then multiply by 2 or 3 until a whole number for every element is obtained.)

	Si	O
Mass (g)	3.50	4.00
Amount (mol)	$\frac{3.5}{28.1} = 0.125$	$\frac{4.0}{16.0} = 0.250$
Mole ratio	$\frac{0.125}{0.125} = 1$	$\frac{0.25}{0.125} = 2$
Empirical formula	Si_1	O_2
	which we write as **SiO_2**	

✔*Quick check 1*

Empirical formula from the mass of one reactant and the mass of product

■ WORKED EXAMPLE

Calculate the empirical formula of iron bromide if 3.78 g of iron reacts with bromine to give 20.0 g of iron bromide.

STEP 1 First find the mass of bromine combined with the iron, by subtracting the mass of iron from the mass of product:

mass of bromine = 20.0 – 3.78 = 16.22 g

STEP 2 Then work out the mole ratio of the reactants as before.

	Fe	Br
Mass (g)	3.78	16.22
Amount (mol)	$\frac{3.78}{55.8} = 0.0677$	$\frac{16.22}{79.9} = 0.203$
Mole ratio	$\frac{0.0677}{0.0677} = 1$	$\frac{0.203}{0.0677} = 3$
Empirical formula	Fe_1	Br_3
	which we write as **$FeBr_3$**	

Empirical formula from the percentage composition by mass

Sometimes the percentage of each reactant is given instead of its mass. In this case, assume you have 100 g of the compound. The percentage of the element then becomes its mass in g.

✓ *Quick check 3, 4*

■ WORKED EXAMPLE

Calculate the empirical formula of a compound consisting of 47.5% sulfur and 52.6% chlorine by mass.

STEP 1 Assume 100 g of compound, so mass of S = 47.5 g and mass of Cl = 52.5 g.

STEP 2 Continue the calculation as usual.

	S	Cl
Mass (g)	47.5	52.5
Amount (mol)	$\frac{47.5}{32.1} = 1.48$	$\frac{52.5}{35.5} = 1.48$
Mole ratio	1	1
Empirical formula	S_1	Cl_1
	which we write as **SCl**	

Molecular formula

If the **relative molecular mass** is known, the molecular formula can be worked out from the empirical formula.

✓ *Quick check 2*

■ WORKED EXAMPLE

In the example above, if the relative molecular mass is 135.2, find the molecular formula.

STEP 1 Calculate the relative mass of the empirical formula.

$$M_r = 32.1 + 35.5 = 67.6$$

STEP 2 Let the molecular formula be $(SCl) \times n$.

STEP 3 Then
$$(SCl) \times n = 135.2$$
$$67.6 \times n = 135.2$$
$$n = 135.2/67.6 = 2$$

So the molecular formula is S_2Cl_2.

QUICK CHECK QUESTIONS

1   Calculate the empirical formula of the substance which, on analysis, is found to contain 0.42 g C, 0.110 g H and 0.29 g O.

2   Dibutyl succinate is a domestic insect repellent. Its composition is 62.58% C, 9.63% H and 27.79% O. Its relative molecular mass is 230. What are the empirical and molecular formulae of dibutyl succinate?

3   Three compounds formed between iron and oxygen have the percentage compositions shown to the right.

Calculate the empirical formulae of all three compounds.

4   A compound containing sodium and oxygen contains 59% by mass of sodium and 41% by mass of oxygen.
Calculate the empirical formula of the compound.

Compound	Percentage iron	Percentage oxygen
A	69.9	30.1
B	77.7	22.3
C	72.3	27.7

Acids, bases and salts

Key words

- acid
- base
- neutralisation
- exothermic
- carbonate

✓ *Quick check 1*

Examiner tip

Learn the common acids and bases listed in these tables.

Hint

This is also a dissociation, because the sodium hydroxide splits up in aqueous solution.

✓ *Quick check 2*

Acids and bases are very important compounds. In this spread we will revise how they can be defined, and their reactions.

Acids

- An H^+ ion is a hydrogen atom minus its electron, therefore it is a proton.
- Acids release H^+ ions in solution. For example, hydrochloric acid, HCl, dissociates (splits up) in aqueous solution as follows:

$$HCl(aq) \rightarrow H^+(aq) + Cl^-(aq)$$

- The three most commonly used acids are shown in the table below:

Acid	Formula
Hydrochloric	HCl
Sulfuric	H_2SO_4
Nitric	HNO_3

Bases

- Bases are the oxides or hydroxides of metals and ammonia.
- Alkalis are soluble bases and they release OH^- ions in aqueous solution. For example, sodium hydroxide:

$$NaOH(aq) \rightarrow Na^+(aq) + OH^-(aq)$$

- Three commonly used bases are shown in the table below:

Base	Formula
Sodium hydroxide	NaOH
Potassium hydroxide	KOH
Ammonia	NH_3

- Bases accept H^+ ions from acids. For example, OH^- ions from alkalis will react with H^+ ions to give water:

$$H^+(aq) + OH^-(aq) \rightarrow H_2O(l)$$

- Aqueous ammonia will accept an H^+ ion to give ammonium, NH_4^+, ions:

$$H^+(aq) + NH_3(aq) \rightarrow NH_4^+(aq)$$

Salts

- Salts are produced when the hydrogen ions in an acid are wholly or partially replaced by metal or ammonium ions.
- Examples of salts are given in the table below:

Acid	Metal or ammonium ion	Name and formula of salt formed	Comment/explanation
H_2SO_4	Mg^{2+}	Magnesium sulfate, $MgSO_4$	Both H^+ ions in the acid are replaced. Salts of sulfuric acid are sulfates.
H_2SO_4	Na^+	Sodium hydrogen/sulfate, $NaHSO_4$	Only one of the H^+ ions is replaced.
H_2SO_4	Na^+	Sodium sulfate, Na_2SO_4	Both the H^+ ions are replaced.
HNO_3	Na^+	Sodium nitrate, $NaNO_3$	Salts of nitric acid are nitrates.
HCl	NH_4^+	Ammonium chloride, NH_4Cl	Salts of hydrochloric acid are chlorides.

The reactions of acids

Acids are a group of substances with similar properties, and with certain substances their reactions can be accurately predicted – a case of 'know one, know them all'.

In the exam, you may be asked to state the products of these reactions and the observations you would make.

Module 1

With carbonates:

- Acids react with carbonates to form carbon dioxide gas, a salt and water.
- You can predict the salt formed from the metal and the acid present.
- The general equation is: **acid + carbonate → salt + carbon dioxide + water**
- If the salt formed is soluble, the following observations can be predicted without you even doing the experiment:

  the carbonate disappears into the solution

  there is effervescence (fizzing) because of the carbon dioxide formed.

For example: $Na_2CO_3(s) + 2HCl(aq) \rightarrow 2NaCl(aq) + H_2O(l) + CO_2(g)$

✓ Quick check 3

With bases and alkalis:

- With bases and alkalis the products are *water* and a *salt*.
- The general equation is: **acid + base or alkali → salt + water**
- This is a neutralisation reaction.
- With insoluble bases, the base reacts with the acid to form a salt and water. It is also an **exothermic** reaction. You will see the solid disappear as it reacts.

Example: $CuO(s) + H_2SO_4(aq) \rightarrow CuSO_4(aq) + H_2O(l)$

- With alkalis, no observations can be made apart from the fact that there is an exothermic reaction.

Example: $NaOH(aq) + HCl(aq) \rightarrow NaCl(aq) + H_2O(l)$

> **Hint**
>
> Bases must have lone-pair electrons to accept the H^+ ions and form a dative covalent bond.

With reactive metals:

- Acids react with reactive metals to form a salt plus hydrogen gas.
- The general equation is: **reactive metal + acid → salt + hydrogen**
- Effervescence is observed because a gas is produced.

Example: $Mg + 2HCl \rightarrow MgCl_2 + H_2$

✓ Quick check 4

QUICK CHECK QUESTIONS

1 a Give the equations for the dissociation of nitric acid and sulfuric acid in aqueous solution.
   b How do your equations explain that both substances are acids?

2 a Give the equations for the dissociation of potassium hydroxide and calcium hydroxide in aqueous solution.
   b How do your equations explain that both substances are alkalis?

3 Complete and balance the following equations, and give the *main* observation you would make *for all of them* if you did the experiment:
   a $CaCO_3(s) + HNO_3(aq) \rightarrow$ b $ZnCO_3(s) + H_2SO_4(aq) \rightarrow$
   c $MgCO_3(s) + HCl(aq) \rightarrow$

4 Complete and balance the following equations:
   a $CaO(s) + HNO_3(aq) \rightarrow$ b $ZnO(s) + HCl(aq) \rightarrow$
   c $NH_3(aq) + H_2SO_4(aq) \rightarrow$

Water of crystallisation and titration calculations

Key words
- water of crystallisation
- titration

This section requires you to do some calculations.

Water of crystallisation

- When salts crystallise from solution, they often form **hydrated** salts containing loosely bonded water molecules. This is called **water of crystallisation**, and is written with a dot next to the number of water molecules in the formula.

Example:

A formula unit of hydrated copper sulfate has five molecules of water of crystallisation, $CuSO_4 \cdot 5H_2O$

- A salt with water attached is hydrated.

- This water is easily removed by heating to form an **anhydrous** salt.

Example:

When heated, copper sulfate crystals ($CuSO_4 \cdot 5H_2O$) lose their water of crystallisation to form anhydrous copper sulfate, $CuSO_4$.

Calculations involving water of crystallisation

There are two main types of question.

Type 1: From percentage composition.

■ WORKED EXAMPLE

What is the formula of hydrated magnesium sulfate crystals that contain $MgSO_4$ (48.8%) and H_2O (51.2%)?

M of $MgSO_4 = 120.3\,g\,mol^{-1}$;
M of $H_2O = 18.0\,g\,mol^{-1}$

We use the same method as for other empirical formulae calculations.

STEP 1 Assume 100 g of compound, so mass of $MgSO_4 = 48.8\,g$ and mass of $H_2O = 51.2\,g$

STEP 2 Continue the calculation as usual.

	MgSO₄	H₂O
Mass in g	48.8	51.2
Number of moles	$\frac{48.8}{120.3} = 0.406$	$\frac{51.2}{18} = 2.84$
Mole ratio	1	7
Empirical formula	MgSO₄	7H₂O
Formula	MgSO₄·7H₂O	

✔*Quick check 1*

Type 2: From masses and experimental data.

■ WORKED EXAMPLE

When 4.76 g of hydrated cobalt chloride crystals were heated they gave 2.6 g of anhydrous cobalt chloride ($CoCl_2$). What is the formula of the hydrated salt? (Co = 58.9; Cl = 35.5; H = 1.0; O = 16.0)

STEP 1 Calculate M of cobalt chloride and water. These come to 129.9 and 18.0 g mol⁻¹, respectively.

STEP 2 Calculate the mass of water in the sample.

mass of water = 4.76 − 2.6 = 2.16 g

STEP 3 Continue calculation.

	CoCl₂	H₂O
Mass in g	2.60	2.16
Number of moles	$\frac{2.60}{129.9} = 0.02$	$\frac{2.16}{18} = 0.12$
Mole ratio	1	6
Empirical formula	CoCl₂	6H₂O
Formula	CoCl₂·6H₂O	

✔*Quick check 2*

Titration calculations

These often cause problems. One way of solving them successfully is to follow this plan, and set out the calculations underneath each reactant or product in the equation.

■ WORKED EXAMPLE

A student doing a titration found that $12.5\,cm^3$ of $0.0200\,mol\,dm^{-3}$ aqueous KOH exactly neutralised $25.0\,cm^3$ of nitric acid. What is the concentration of the nitric acid?

STEP 1 Construct the equation:

$$KOH(aq) + HNO_3(aq) \rightarrow KNO_3(aq) + H_2O(l)$$

You are only interested in the KOH and the HNO_3.

STEP 2 Write down what you know.

	KOH	HNO₃
Volume (cm³)	12.5	25.0
Concentration (mol dm⁻³)	0.0200	?

STEP 3 Calculate the amount, in mol of KOH.

$$\text{amount (mol)} = \frac{\text{volume}}{1000} \times \text{concentration} = \frac{12.5}{1000} \times 0.0200 = 2.50 \times 10^{-4}\,\text{mol}$$

STEP 4 Work out the number of moles of HNO_3 by looking at the equation.

$$\text{amount (mol)} = 2.50 \times 10^{-4}$$

1 mol KOH reacts with 1 mol HNO_3 (1:1 stoichiometry in the equation).

STEP 5 Work out the concentration of the HNO_3

$$\text{concentration} = \frac{\text{amount (mol)}}{\text{volume (dm}^3)} = \frac{(2.50 \times 10^{-4})}{(25.0/1000)} = 0.0100\ \text{mol dm}^{-3}$$

✔ *Quick check 3*

QUICK CHECK QUESTIONS

1   Find the formulae of the hydrated salts of sodium carbonate with the following percentage composition by mass:
   a Na_2CO_3 (59.6%) and water (40.4%)
   b Na_2CO_3 (37.1%) and water (62.9%)
   (M_r of $Na_2CO_3 = 106.0$; $H_2O = 18.0$)

2   When 5.56 g of iron(II) sulfate crystals are gently heated they form 3.04 g of the anhydrous salt. What is the empirical formula of the hydrated salt?
   (M of $FeSO_4 = 151.9\,g\,mol^{-1}$)

3   A sample of $10.00\,cm^3$ of $0.0700\,mol\,dm^{-3}$ sulfuric acid required exactly $23.00\,cm^3$ of aqueous sodium hydroxide to neutralise it. Calculate the concentration of the aqueous sodium hydroxide.

4   What volume of $0.100\,mol\,dm^{-3}$ aqueous sodium hydroxide is required to neutralise $25.0\,cm^3$ of $0.200\,mol\,dm^{-3}$ hydrochloric acid?

UNIT 1

Oxidation and reduction

Key words

- reduction
- oxidation
- redox
- oxidation number

Oxidation and reduction always occur at the same time. Reactions where this happens are called **redox reactions** (**red**uction and **ox**idation). You may have come across these definitions:

- oxidation as the gain of oxygen; reduction as the loss of oxygen
- oxidation as the loss of hydrogen; reduction as the gain of hydrogen.

Now we will describe redox reactions in two new ways – electron transfer and oxidation state (**oxidation number**).

Electron transfer

Look at an oxidation reaction for a typical Group 2 element, magnesium:

$$2Mg(s) + O_2(g) \rightarrow 2MgO(s)$$

In this reaction,

$Mg \rightarrow Mg^{2+} + 2e^-$, which shows us that magnesium has lost electrons. The magnesium has been **oxidised**.

- Oxidation is defined as the loss of electrons.

$O_2 + 4e^- \rightarrow 2O^{2-}$, which shows us that oxygen has gained electrons. The oxygen has been **reduced**.

- Reduction is defined as the gain of electrons.

Hint

Remember OILRIG:
Oxidation Is Loss
of e⁻s
Reduction Is Gain
of e⁻s.

Oxidation number (oxidation state)

Oxidation numbers (ONs) are *the number of electrons that atoms lose, gain or share* when they form bonds with other elements. An oxidation number can be positive, negative or zero.

They are assigned to each atom in a compound or element. They are useful because:

- oxidation means an increase in oxidation number – ON becomes more positive
- reduction means a decrease in oxidation number – ON becomes more negative.

✔Quick check 1

How to assign oxidation numbers

Follow these rules, and if two rules appear to contradict each other *follow the one that is higher in the list.*

✔Quick check 2

- The oxidation number of an atom in the free element is zero.
- The total of the oxidation states of all the atoms in a compound is zero.
- The oxidation number of monatomic ions is the same as the charge on the ion.
- In a polyatomic ion, such as SO_4^{2-}, the total of the ONs of all the atoms in the ion equals the charge on the ion.
- In compounds, Group 1 metals have an ON of +1.
- In compounds, Group 2 metals have an ON of +2.
- In compounds, H has an ON of +1.
- In compounds, F has an ON of –1.
- In compounds, O has an ON of –2.
- In compounds with metals, Group 7 elements (Cl, Br, I) have an ON of –1.
- In compounds with metals, Group 6 elements (O, S) have an ON of –2.
- In covalent compounds, the more electronegative element has the negative ON (page 26).

Examiner tip

Remember that metals generally lose electrons to form positive ions, with an increase in oxidation number; non-metals usually react by gaining electrons to form negative ions, with a decrease in oxidation number.

✓ *Quick check 3 and 4*

Module 1

■ WORKED EXAMPLE

Find the oxidation number of the underlined element in the following.

a $\underline{Cl}_2$

This is the formula of the element chlorine. Uncombined elements have ON = 0. We can write this as $Cl_2(0)$.

b $\underline{Al}_2O_3$

The total of the ON of all the atoms = 0. The ON of oxygen, O, = –2. The total for three O atoms is –6. The total for two Al atoms is +6. Therefore ON of aluminium = +3.

c $\underline{Mn}O_4^-$

The total of the ON of all the atoms is –1. The ON of oxygen, O, is –2. The total for four O atoms is –8. The ON of manganese is +7.

d $H_2\underline{O}$

The total of the ON of all the atoms is 0. The ON of hydrogen = +1 and there are two of them, giving a total of +2. The ON of O is –2.

e $H_2\underline{O}_2$

The total of the ON of all the atoms is 0. The ON of hydrogen = +1. The total for two H atoms is +2, so the total for two O atoms is –2. The ON of O is –1 (remember, if two rules appear to contradict each other, follow the one higher in the list).

f $Na_3\underline{N}$

The total of the ON of all the atoms is 0. The ON of sodium is +1 and there are three of them, giving a total of +3. The ON of N is –3.

> ### Examiner tip
>
> Remember that oxidation numbers must always have a sign (except 0).

Systematic names

In systematic names, the oxidation number is shown in brackets using Roman numerals:

- SO_3^{2-} is sulfate(IV)
- SO_4^{2-} is sulfate(VI)
- $FeCl_2$ is iron(II) chloride
- $FeCl_3$ is iron(III) chloride.

Redox reactions

In chemical reactions between reactive metals and acids (see page 13) a **redox** reaction takes place because the ON of the metal increases from zero to a positive number and the ON of the hydrogen decreases from +1 to zero (as the element). For example, when magnesium reacts with hydrochloric acid, the ON of the magnesium increases from 0 to +2. This increase in ON is balanced by an identical decrease in the ON of the hydrogen.

magnesium	+	hydrochloric acid	→	magnesium chloride	+	hydrogen
Mg	+	2HCl	→	MgCl$_2$	+	H$_2$
ONs 0		2(+1)		+2		0

QUICK CHECK QUESTIONS

1 State four ways of defining reduction. Give an example of one.

2 Work out the oxidation number of
   a sulfur in SO_3^{2-};
   b nitrogen in NH_4^+;
   c carbon in CO_3^{2-}.

3 Allocate oxidation numbers to each atom in the following compounds:
   a NaCl; LiF; SrO
   b magnesium bromide; sodium hydroxide; silver nitrate; sodium sulfate, chlorine.

4 Use oxidation numbers to decide if the underlined atoms are oxidised or reduced in the reaction:
   a $\underline{Mg}(s) + Cl_2(g) \rightarrow MgCl_2(s)$
   b $I_2 + 2\underline{S}_2O_3^{2-} \rightarrow 2I^- + S_4O_6^{2-}$
   c $2\underline{Fe}^{3+} + 2I^- \rightarrow 2Fe^{2+} + I_2$

UNIT 1

Ionisation energy

Examiner tip

Learn the definitions of first and second ionisation energy.

✓ *Quick check 1*

✓ *Quick check 2*

Ionisation is all about removing electrons from atoms to make positive ions.

The **first ionisation energy** is the energy required to remove one electron from each atom in one mole of gaseous atoms to form one mole of gaseous 1+ ions:

$$M(g) \rightarrow M^+(g) + e^-$$

The **second ionisation energy** refers to the removal of the next mole of electrons from the mole of gaseous 1+ ions:

$$M^+(g) \rightarrow M^{2+}(g) + e^-.$$

The third ionisation energy refers to $M^{2+}(g) \rightarrow M^{3+}(g) + e^-$, and so on.

Factors influencing the first ionisation energy

- **Nuclear charge** – a large nuclear charge means the outer electron is difficult to remove, so the ionisation energy is large.
- **Atomic radius** – in larger atoms, the outer electron is farther away from and less strongly attracted by the nucleus, so it is easier to remove and the ionisation energy is lower.
- **Electron shielding** – if more inner electron shells shield the nuclear charge from the outer electron, it will be easier to remove, and the ionisation energy is low.

These facts mean that the ionisation energy:

- *decreases* down a **group** because the atomic radius and electron shielding both increase
- *increases* across a **period** because the nuclear charge increases.

Ionisation energies across a period

Look at the graph of first ionisation energies of the elements in Period 3:

The overall trend is a general increase across the period. This is caused by the increasing nuclear charge attracting the electrons more strongly and therefore making it difficult to remove an electron. The outer electrons of these elements are in the same shell, so atomic radius and electron shielding remain similar across the period.

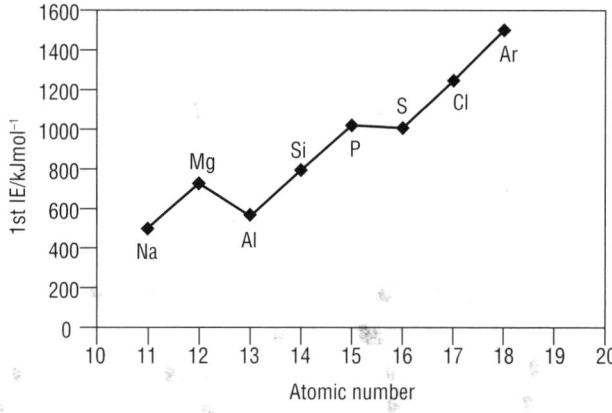

Ionisation energies down a group

- As we go down a group, the first ionisation energy decreases.
- This is because for each successive element, the distance from the nucleus and electron shielding from inner electrons both increase, and these outweigh the effect of increasing nuclear charge.

How to predict electron configurations from ionisation energies

The values of **successive ionisation energies** can tell us the group an element is from. **Successive ionisation energies** (IE) simply mean the first, second, third, etc. IE for one particular element.

The first four successive IEs for sodium look like this (see graph on right):

The first IE is relatively small, then there is a large jump to the second IE. The rest are slightly larger still.

- The first IE refers to removing the outer electron – this is relatively easy to do because it is in the $n=3$ shell, the furthest from the nucleus.
- The second IE refers to removing an electron from the $n=2$ shell – this takes much more energy. This is because the electron is being removed from the next full shell of electrons, which is closer to the nucleus, attracted more strongly and therefore difficult to remove.
- The next two electrons to be removed are also in the second shell, and so they are not much more difficult to remove than the second electron.

Successive IEs for magnesium and aluminium look like this (see graphs):

Magnesium, in Group 2, has two outer ($n=3$) electrons, which are easy to remove, then a large increase in the amount of energy required to remove the next electron, because it is in the next shell ($n=2$).

Aluminium, in Group 3, has three electrons that are easy to remove in the outer shell, so three relatively low IEs.

We can see that the pattern of successive IEs for:

- all Group 1 elements is 1 low IE
- all Group 2 elements is 2 low IEs
- all Group 3 elements is 3 low IEs.

Then there is a large jump in the IE as we enter another shell – the next electron is nearer to the nucleus and has fewer electrons shielding it from the nuclear charge.

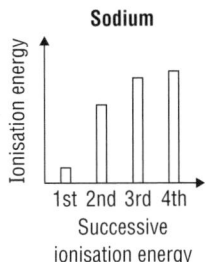

Sodium

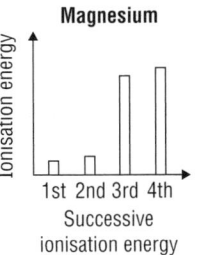

Magnesium

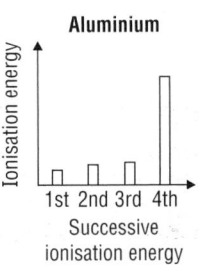

Aluminium

✔ *Quick check 3 and 4*

QUICK CHECK QUESTIONS

1 The first ionisation energy of arsenic, As, is 947 kJ mol^{-1}. Predict the value of the first ionisation energy of bismuth, Bi, in the same group.

2 Explain why the first ionisation energy of As, 947 kJ mol^{-1}, is greater than that of the previous element in the Periodic Table, which is germanium.

3 Sketch the shape of the bar chart of the first six successive ionisation energies for the element carbon. Explain how the data show that carbon is in Group 4.

4 Define first ionisation energy. Name three properties of the atom that influence the size of the ionisation energy. Explain why each property exerts an effect.

Electron configurations – the arrangement of electrons in an atom

Key words

- shell
- sub-shell
- orbital
- electron configuration

Examiner tip

Make sure you understand the difference between shells, sub-shells and orbitals.

Examiner tip

Learn the order in which sub-shells are filled; don't forget 4s is filled before 3d.

- Electrons fill different energy levels, or **shells**, numbered $n = 1, 2, 3$, etc.
- These shells can be subdivided further into **sub-shells**, and the sub-shells are made up of **orbitals** (regions that can hold up to two electrons with opposite spins).
- The sub-shells are called s, p and d sub-shells, and each one holds a different number of electrons.
- This is how the sub-shells are divided between the shells:

Shell	Shell 1	Shell 2		Shell 3		
Sub-shell	s	s	p	s	p	d
Number of orbitals in sub-shell	1	1	3	1	3	5
Maximum number of electrons in sub-shell	2	2	6	2	6	10

For the first 36 elements, the order in which the sub-shells are filled is from the lowest energy level to the highest: 1s, 2s, 2p, 3s, 3p, 4s, 3d, 4p.

In each sub-shell, the electrons go into empty orbitals first, then when they go into half-filled orbitals the electron pairs have opposite spins.

■ WORKED EXAMPLE

Br has 35 electrons: electron configuration $1s^2 2s^2 2p^6 3s^2 3p^6 3d^{10} 4s^2 4p^5$.

NOTE Once the electrons start to fill the 3d sub-shell, the energy of the 3d sub-shell falls below that of the filled 4s sub-shell. The 3d sub-shell is placed first when writing the electron configuration. This is the only anomaly you will have to deal with when writing electron configurations.

Br⁻ has 36 electrons: electron configuration is $1s^2 2s^2 2p^6 3s^2 3p^6 3d^{10} 4s^2 4p^6$
Na⁺ has 10 electrons (Na has 11 electrons): electron configuration is $1s^2 2s^2 2p^6$

✓ *Quick check 1 and 3*

Shapes of the s- and p-orbitals

The s- and p-orbitals have different shapes. The s-orbitals are spherical.

There are three p-orbitals at right angles to each other, and they have a lobed shape.

✓ *Quick check 2*

s-orbital

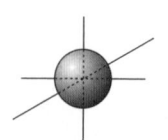

p-orbitals

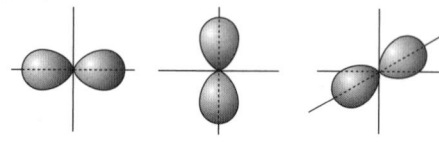

Electron configurations and the Periodic Table

Look at the Periodic Table (see page 30). The elements are arranged in blocks. The block
to which an element belongs depends on its electron arrangement.

Quick check 4

Module 2

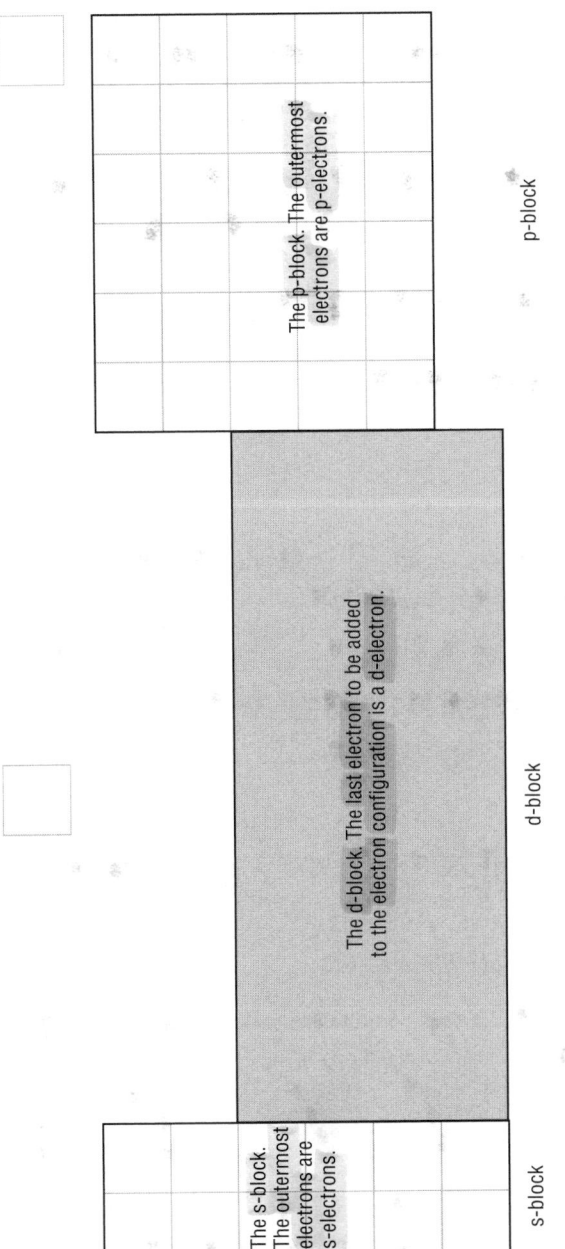

The p-block. The outermost electrons are p-electrons.

p-block

The d-block. The last electron to be added to the electron configuration is a d-electron.

d-block

The s-block. The outermost electrons are s-electrons.

s-block

QUICK CHECK QUESTIONS

1 Write down the electron configurations of the following:
   a a sodium atom   **b** a V atom
   c a K^+ ion   **d** an O^{2-} ion

2 Draw an s-orbital and a p-orbital.

3 Which element has the electron configuration $1s^2\ 2s^2\ 2p^6\ 3s^2$?

4 To which block of the Periodic Table do the following elements belong?
   a the element with the electron configuration $1s^2\ 2s^2\ 2p^6\ 3s^1$.
   b the element with the electron configuration $1s^2\ 2s^2\ 2p^6\ 3s^23p^63d^44s^2$.
   c the element with the electron configuration $1s^2\ 2s^2\ 2p^6\ 3s^23p^63d^{10}4s^24p^5$.

Chemical bonding

Ionic bonding

- This is the bonding usually found in compounds of a metal (Groups 1 and 2) with a non-metal (usually Groups 5–7).
- Ionic bonding is the *electrostatic attraction between oppositely charged ions*.
- It arises when an electron is transferred from one atom to another, forming **ions**.
- The charge on an ion can be predicted from the position of the element in the Periodic Table.
- Groups 1 and 2 (metals) lose electrons to form 1+ or 2+ ions depending on the number of electrons lost.
- Groups 5–7 (non-metals) will form 3–, 2– or 1– ions depending on the number of electrons gained.

Example

Potassium chloride, KCl, has ionic bonding. It is composed of K^+ and Cl^- ions. These ions are formed from the atoms by the loss or gain of an electron.

The K atom has one electron in the outermost 4s sub-shell.

The Cl atom has seven electrons in its outermost 3s and 3p sub-shells.

The K atom loses an electron to become the potassium ion:

$$K \rightarrow K^+ + e^-$$

and this electron is transferred to the chlorine atom which becomes a chloride ion:

$$Cl + e^- \rightarrow Cl^-.$$

By doing this, both achieve a *full outer shell of eight electrons*.

We can show ionic bonding using dot-and-cross diagrams: dots indicate electrons of one atom; crosses indicate electrons of the other atom. A dot-and-cross diagram of the formation of KCl looks like this:

Only the outer electrons are shown. Here are the dot-and-cross diagrams for two ionic structures, sodium chloride and magnesium oxide (left).

Solid ionic compounds have a giant lattice structure, where each ion is surrounded by ions of opposite charge and is held in place by the attraction between them.

Sodium chloride

$$Na \rightarrow Na^+ + e^-$$

$$Cl + e^- \rightarrow Cl^-$$

Magnesium oxide

$$Mg \rightarrow Mg^{2+} + 2e^-$$

$$O + 2e^- \rightarrow O^{2-}$$

Covalent bonding

- This is the bonding usually found in compounds of a non-metal with another non-metal (usually hydrogen and Groups 4–7).
- Covalent bonding is the *sharing of a pair of electrons* between two atoms.
- In a covalent bond, *one electron comes from each atom*. We can show covalent bonding using dot-and-cross diagrams.

For example, chlorine gas, Cl_2, has covalent bonding.

Both Cl atoms have seven electrons in the outer sub-shells. Two Cl atoms combine so that each shares the single electron of the other. Both chlorine atoms then have a full outer shell of eight electrons (a noble gas configuration). A covalent bond is represented by a single line, so chlorine, Cl_2, is written as Cl–Cl.

In covalent compounds, it is possible for two atoms to share more than one pair of electrons. Sharing two pairs of electrons gives a double bond.

Sharing three pairs of electrons gives a triple bond.

$$\overset{\bullet}{\underset{\bullet}{\times}}N\overset{\bullet}{\underset{\bullet}{\times}}N\overset{\bullet}{\underset{\bullet}{\colon}} \qquad N\equiv N$$

✔ *Quick check 2*

Learn the dot-and-cross diagrams for these covalent compounds					
Hydrogen H_2	H–H	H•H	Methane CH_4	H–C–H (with H above and below)	dot-and-cross diagram
Oxygen O_2	O=O	dot-and-cross diagram	Carbon dioxide CO_2	O=C=O	dot-and-cross diagram
Hydrogen chloride HCl	H–Cl	dot-and-cross diagram	Ethene $H_2C=CH_2$	structural diagram	dot-and-cross diagram

Dative covalent bonding

✔ *Quick check 3, 4, 5*

- This is a particular type of covalent bonding.
- In a **dative covalent** bond, both the electrons in the bond, the bonded pair, are supplied by *one atom* only.
- Dative covalent bonds are sometimes called **coordinate bonds**.

Example: NH_4^+ has dative covalent bonding in one of the bonds between the N and H atoms, shown by an arrow.

How can we decide which type of bond, ionic or covalent, is formed between two elements?

One way is to look at the Periodic Table (see diagram opposite).

- If one atom comes from section A of the diagram and the other from section B, then an ionic bond is formed.
- If both atoms come from section B, a covalent bond is formed.
- It is more difficult to predict what will happen if the elements come from other sections.

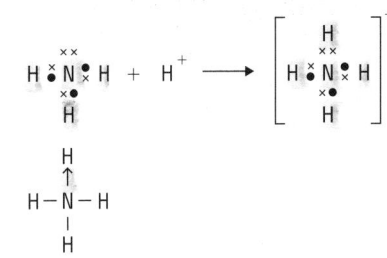

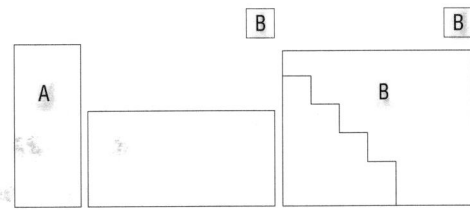

Module 2

QUICK CHECK QUESTIONS

1 Draw dot-and-cross diagrams (outer electrons only) for:
   a KBr   b $MgCl_2$ c Na_3N

2 Draw dot-and-cross diagrams for:
   a C_2H_6 b H_2O c N_2 d NH_3

3 Draw dot-and-cross diagrams for
   a NH_4^+ b H_3O^+ c BF_3

4 Look at the dot-and-cross diagrams for NH_3 and BF_3. How could these compounds be bonded together by a dative covalent bond?

5 What is the difference between covalent bonding and dative covalent bonding?

Shapes of molecules – electron-pair repulsion theory

Key words

- electron-pair repulsion
- covalent bond
- lone pair

Electron pairs repel each other so they are as far apart as possible. In a **covalent** compound or ion, the number of electron pairs around the central atom determines the shape of the molecule.

Number of pairs	Shape	Example
2 electron pairs	linear	CO_2 (in fact two double bonds) Bond angle 180°
3 electron pairs	trigonal	BF_3 Bond angle 120°
4 electron pairs	tetrahedral	CH_4 NH_4^+ Bond angle 109.5°
6 electron pairs	octahedral	SF_6 Bond angle 90°

We know the different shapes of molecules by working out how the electron pairs arrange themselves in space. The rules of electron-pair repulsion theory tell us that:

- electron pairs repel each other so they are as far apart as possible
- an electron pair shared between two atoms is called a bonding pair (BP)
- a non-bonding pair on one atom only (not shared) is called a lone pair (LP)
- LP–LP repulsion > LP–BP repulsion > BP–BP repulsion.

These rules explain the shapes of the ammonia, NH_3, and water, H_2O, molecules.

NH_3

The nitrogen atom has four pairs of electrons, so these will take up a basically tetrahedral shape. But one electron pair is a lone pair, so it repels the shared pairs more than a bonding pair would, and the bond angle is decreased from 109.5° to 107°. The final shape of the molecule is described as pyramidal.

✔ *Quick check 1*

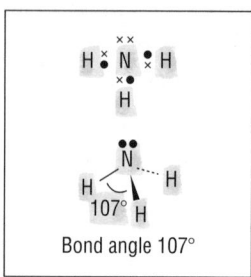

Bond angle 107°

H_2O

The oxygen atom has four pairs of electrons, so these will take up a basically tetrahedral shape. But two of the electron pairs are lone pairs, so the shared pairs are repelled more than in NH_3, and the bond angle in H_2O is less than in NH_3. The final bond angle is 104.5°. The final shape of the molecule is described as non-linear.

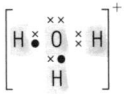

Bond angle 104.5°

■ WORKED EXAMPLE

To work out the shape of an ion, for example H_3O^+:

STEP 1 There are two ways to approach this problem.

either draw a dot-and-cross diagram of the molecule (see diagram opposite);

or count up the number of electrons at the central atom.

Atom	Number of electrons
Oxygen	6
Three hydrogens	3
Positive charge	–1
Total number	8

STEP 2 See what shape the electron pairs will adopt. They will be arranged tetrahedrally because there are four pairs of electrons.

STEP 3 Now see if there are any lone pairs. Yes, one lone pair.

STEP 4 Electron-pair repulsion theory tells you that the lone pair will repel the bonding pairs a little more strongly than they repel each other, and the molecule should have the same shape and bond angle as NH_3.

H_3O^+ has a pyramidal shape with a bond angle of 107°.

✓*Quick check 2*

Module 2

What about multiple bonds?

If a molecule has double (or triple) bonds, the bonding electron pairs are all located between the bonding atoms and therefore they count as one bonding pair of electrons around the central atom for working out the shape.

CO_2

A dot-and-cross diagram of CO_2 shows that the bonding is O=C=O (see table). The electron pairs in the double bonds will repel each other as much as possible, so the final shape of the molecule is linear.

What about a non-linear molecule with double bonds? A good example is sulfur dioxide (see quick check question 3).

✓*Quick check 3*

QUICK CHECK QUESTIONS

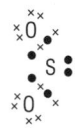

1 Sketch the shapes and predict the bond angles in the following molecules:
  a PCl_3
  b OCl_2
  c SeF_6 (note that Se is in Group 6)
  d CCl_4

2 Sketch the shapes and predict the bond angles in the following ions:
  a PCl_4^+
  b PCl_6^-
  c NH_2^-
  d NH_4^+

3 The dot-and-cross diagram for SO_2 is shown in the diagram opposite.
  a What is the shape of the molecule?
  b Give the approximate bond angle.

Electronegativity, polarity and intermolecular forces

Key words

- electronegativity
- van der Waals' forces
- hydrogen bonding
- induced dipole
- instantaneous

Hint

Halogen atoms generally have high electronegativity.

Hint

A bond is polar if there is a large difference in electronegativity between the atoms.

✓ *Quick check 1*

A polar bond is a bond with a charge separation. It occurs in **covalent** molecules, and when it does we say the molecule has a **permanent dipole**.

Polarisation of the bond in covalent molecules

Hydrogen chloride, H–Cl

$$\overset{\delta+}{H} - \overset{\delta-}{Cl}$$

- The $\delta+$ sign and the $\delta-$ sign mean the electrons are not evenly distributed between the two atoms, but are concentrated on the Cl atom. This is because Cl attracts electrons more than H.
- We say that chlorine has a greater **electronegativity** than hydrogen.

Electronegativity is the ability of an atom to attract the bonding electrons in a covalent bond.

Bond polarisation means that the covalent bond is becoming slightly ionic in character, because it has a dipole moment (charge separation).

Chlorine, Cl–Cl

In this molecule, both atoms have the same electronegativity so there is no bond polarisation.

Summary

- Bond polarisation occurs in **covalent** compounds. It arises because the two atoms sharing a bond have different electronegativities.
- Polarisation shows us that ionic bonds and covalent bonds are the two extremes of bonding types, and there is a gradual range of bonding in between.

Intermolecular forces

These are weak forces that arise *between* molecules. They are *short-range* forces.

- **Permanent dipole–dipole forces** occur between molecules with a permanent dipole. The $\delta+$ atom on one molecule attracts the $\delta-$ atom on a neighbouring molecule, so electrostatic attractions operate between the molecules.

Examples are H–Cl, H–Br, H–I, SO_2.

- Instantaneous dipole–induced dipole forces occur between all atoms and molecules, but are significant only where there are a lot of electrons. They are also called **van der Waals' forces**. They are stronger for long, sausage-shaped molecules than for small, round ones.

Examples are the noble gases, the halogens and long polymer chains. These forces are the weakest type of intermolecular force.

- **Hydrogen bonding** is a relatively strong type of permanent dipole–permanent dipole attraction that occurs between molecules containing H attached to either N, O or F.

- These molecules have a permanent dipole, so the $\delta+$ H atoms are attracted to the $\delta-$ N, O or F atoms, and a hydrogen bond is formed.

- We represent hydrogen bonds by showing dashed lines between the atoms concerned. Hydrogen bonds are stronger than permanent dipole–permanent dipole attractions because the N, O and F atoms are highly electronegative.

- Examples of molecules that show hydrogen bonding are NH_3, H_2O and HF.

✓*Quick check 2 and 3*

Examiner tip

Students often forget that H-bonding occurs *only with N, O and F* – no other atoms!

H_2O and hydrogen bonding

Water behaves strangely ... because of its hydrogen bonds. A water molecule can form two hydrogen bonds to other water molecules.

- Water has a relatively high boiling point compared with the other hydrides in Group 6 because hydrogen bonds have to be broken before water molecules can evaporate.

- Water has a high surface tension and forms a meniscus because the hydrogen bonds pull the water surface downwards.

- When water freezes into ice, a whole network of hydrogen bonds forms. The hydrogen bonds and covalent O–H bonds are arranged tetrahedrally around the O atom. The H_2O molecules are kept apart to form a lattice by this arrangement, and there is a lot of space in the structure – this gives ice a *lower density* than water.

✓*Quick check 4 and 5*

Module 2

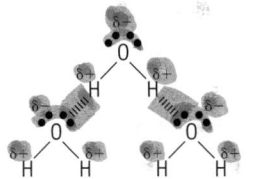

QUICK CHECK QUESTIONS

1 Which of the following molecules are polar? Show where the dipole is on the molecule. HI; PCl_3; CH_4.

2 Predict the main type of intermolecular force in molecules (a–c) below. For each one, explain your answer.
   a C_3H_8 b NH_2OH
   c PCl_3

3 Draw a diagram showing the hydrogen bonds in the alcohol ethanol, C_2H_5OH.

4 Suggest a reason why ethanol has a much higher boiling point than methoxymethane, CH_3OCH_3, which has the same molecular formula.

5 Water is a liquid at room temperature while H_2S is a gas, even though H_2S has a higher molecular mass. Explain.

Structures and physical properties

The main types of structure you must know about are giant ionic lattices, simple molecular substances, giant covalent lattices and metallic lattices.

- Giant ionic lattices have ionic bonding.
- Simple molecular and giant molecular structures have covalent bonding.
- Metals have metallic bonding.

Giant ionic lattices

- Examples are found in NaCl, $MgCl_2$, MgO, Na_2O, NaOH, KBr.
- Ionic compounds have a giant lattice structure of positive and negative ions, held in place by strong electrostatic attraction between the oppositely charged ions.

○ −
● +

Simple molecular lattices

- Examples are N_2, H_2O, I_2 and P_4.
- Simple molecular substances have individual molecules with strong covalent bonding. There are only weak intermolecular forces between molecules because they have no overall charge.

Diatomic gas molecules

Giant covalent (giant molecular) lattices

- Examples are diamond, graphite (within layers, not between layers) and silicon dioxide.
- Giant molecular substances have a giant lattice of atoms linked together with strong covalent bonds throughout the lattice.

Giant metallic lattices

- Examples include Cu, Mg, Na, Al.
- Metallic structures are composed of a lattice of positive ions in a sea of mobile, delocalised electrons. Electrostatic attraction between the delocalised electrons and the positive ions holds the structure together. This is called metallic bonding.

  The outermost electron shells overlap each other and the electrons are *delocalised*. The electrons in the outer shells can therefore travel from atom to atom, and positive ions are left in their lattice position.

✔ *Quick check 1*

How the physical properties of a substance are linked to its structure

Giant ionic structures

Physical properties	Explanation
High melting point	Strong electrostatic attraction between ions so a lot of energy is needed to break these bonds
No electrical conductivity when solid	Ions are fixed in the lattice and therefore cannot move and carry current
Good electrical conductivity when molten or aqueous	Ions can move in liquid or solution, so can carry electrical current
Dissolve well in polar solvents such as water	Polar solvent molecules attract ions out of the lattice into solution

Simple molecular structures

Physical properties	Explanation
Low melting point	Molecules are held together by weak intermolecular forces that can be overcome with relatively little energy
No electrical conductivity	No free electrons or ions

Giant covalent structures

Physical properties	Explanation
Very high melting point	All the atoms are joined together by strong covalent bonds, so it takes a lot of energy to break all these bonds
No electrical conductivity	Electrons are fixed in the covalent bonds, so cannot move to carry current

Giant metallic structures

Physical properties	Explanation
Generally high melting point (but not as high generally as giant covalent structures)	Electrostatic attraction between positive ions and delocalised electrons is strong so a lot of energy is needed to break these bonds
Good electrical conductivity	Electrons are mobile, so are free to carry a current

✔ *Quick check 2 and 3*

QUICK CHECK QUESTIONS

1 Name the type of structure in:
   a NaBr
   b K
   c Kr
   d CH_4

2 Silicon dioxide, SiO_2, is commonly known as sand. From your knowledge of the physical properties of sand, suggest the structure of SiO_2 and explain your answer.

3 The table below shows the properties of four substances. Complete the table.

Substance	Particles present	Melting point	Electrical conductivity:		Type of structure
			of solid	of liquid	
A	(a)	Low	(b)	(c)	Simple molecular
B	(d)	High	Poor	Poor	(e)
C	(f)	High	Good	Good	(g)
D	ions	(h)	(i)	(j)	(k)

Module 2

UNIT 1

The Periodic Table

Module 3

Key words

- groups
- periods

✓ *Quick check 1*

Examiner tip

Remember, Z = number of protons in an atom = number of electrons.

✓ *Quick check 2 and 4*

✓ *Quick check 3*

The Periodic Table of the elements comes in various shapes and forms, but the one you will use in the examinations is shown on page 31.

Make sure you are familiar with the names and positions of the main **groups** (elements in the same column) and the numbering of the **periods** (elements in the same row).

- Elements in the same group have *similar* physical and chemical properties.
- Elements in the same period have *repeating* physical and chemical properties.
- The elements are arranged by increasing **atomic number, Z**.
- The Periodic Table can be divided into blocks according to the electron configurations of the elements.

The s-block contains those elements with outer electrons in the s **sub-shell** – Groups 1 and 2.

The p-block contains those elements with outer electrons in the p sub-shell – Groups 3–8.

The d-block contains those elements in which the last electron to be added goes into the d sub-shell – mostly the transition metals.

The position of the element in the Periodic Table tells you how many electrons it has. This is because the elements of each group have the same outer electron configuration. This is why elements of the same group have similar chemical properties.

■ WORKED EXAMPLE

Look at silicon, Si, in the Periodic Table. What is its electron configuration?

STEP 1 Silicon has full electron shells up to the configuration of neon, the noble gas in the period above it. We can represent this by writing [Ne] instead of $1s^2\ 2s^2\ 2p^6$.

STEP 2 Silicon is in Group 4, so it has $ns^2\ np^2$ as its outer electron configuration.

STEP 3 Silicon is in Period 3, so the electron configuration of the outer electrons begins with 3.

STEP 4 The electron configuration is therefore [Ne] $3s^2\ 3p^2$.

QUICK CHECK QUESTIONS

1 What name is given to:
   a a vertical column in the Periodic Table?
   b a horizontal row in the Periodic Table?

2 Explain why the p-block of the Periodic Table is given this name.

3 Write down the electron configurations of the elements A–D in the diagram opposite.

4 An element, X, has the electron arrangement [Kr]$5s^2$. In which block of the Periodic Table would you find the element?

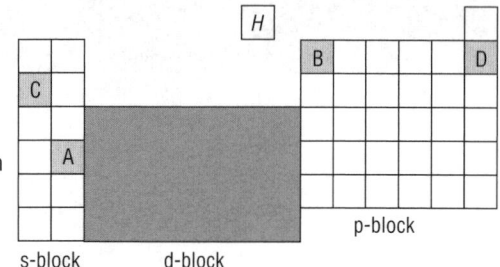

The Periodic Table of the Elements

1	2											3	4	5	6	7	0
					Key Relative atomic mass **Atomic symbol** Name Atomic (proton) number		1.0 **H** Hydrogen 1										4.0 **He** Helium 2
6.9 **Li** Lithium 3	9.0 **Be** Beryllium 4											10.8 **B** Boron 5	12.0 **C** Carbon 6	14.0 **N** Nitrogen 7	16.0 **O** Oxygen 8	19.0 **F** Fluorine 9	20.2 **Ne** Neon 10
23.0 **Na** Sodium 11	24.3 **Mg** Magnesium 12											27.0 **Al** Aluminium 13	28.1 **Si** Silicon 14	31.0 **P** Phosphorus 15	32.1 **S** Sulfur 16	35.5 **Cl** Chlorine 17	39.9 **Ar** Argon 18
39.1 **K** Potassium 19	40.1 **Ca** Calcium 20	45.0 **Sc** Scandium 21	47.9 **Ti** Titanium 22	50.9 **V** Vanadium 23	52.0 **Cr** Chromium 24	54.9 **Mn** Manganese 25	55.8 **Fe** Iron 26	58.9 **Co** Cobalt 27	58.7 **Ni** Nickel 28	63.5 **Cu** Copper 29	65.4 **Zn** Zinc 30	69.7 **Ga** Gallium 31	72.6 **Ge** Germanium 32	74.9 **As** Arsenic 33	79.0 **Se** Selenium 34	79.9 **Br** Bromine 35	83.8 **Kr** Krypton 36
85.5 **Rb** Rubidium 37	87.6 **Sr** Strontium 38	88.9 **Y** Yttrium 39	91.2 **Zr** Zirconium 40	92.9 **Nb** Niobium 41	95.9 **Mo** Molybdenum 42	(98) **Tc** Technetium 43	101.1 **Ru** Ruthenium 44	102.9 **Rh** Rhodium 45	106.4 **Pd** Palladium 46	107.9 **Ag** Silver 47	112.4 **Cd** Cadmium 48	114.8 **In** Indium 49	118.7 **Sn** Tin 50	121.8 **Sb** Antimony 51	127.6 **Te** Tellurium 52	126.9 **I** Iodine 53	131.3 **Xe** Xenon 54
132.9 **Cs** Caesium 55	137.3 **Ba** Barium 56	138.9 **La*** Lanthanum 57	178.5 **Hf** Hafnium 72	180.9 **Ta** Tantalum 73	183.8 **W** Tungsten 74	186.2 **Re** Rhenium 75	190.2 **Os** Osmium 76	192.2 **Ir** Iridium 77	195.1 **Pt** Platinum 78	197.0 **Au** Gold 79	200.6 **Hg** Mercury 80	204.4 **Ti** Thallium 81	207.2 **Pb** Lead 82	209.0 **Bi** Bismuth 83	(209) **Po** Polonium 84	(210) **At** Astatine 85	(222) **Rn** Radon 86
(223) **Fr** Francium 87	(226) **Ra** Radium 88	(227) **Ac*** Actinium 89	(261) **Rf** Rutherfordium 104	(262) **Db** Dubnium 105	(266) **Sg** Seaborgium 106	(264) **Bh** Bohrium 107	(277) **Hs** Hassium 108	(268) **Mt** Meitnerium 109	(271) **Ds** Darmstadtium 110	(272) **Rg** Roentgenium 111							

Elements with atomic numbers 112–116 have been reported but not fully authenticated

140.1 **Ce** Cerium 58	140.9 **Pr** Praseodynium 59	144.2 **Nd** Neodymium 60	144.9 **Pm** Promethium 61	150.4 **Sm** Samarium 62	152.0 **Eu** Europium 63	157.2 **Gd** Gadolinium 64	158.9 **Tb** Terbium 65	162.5 **Dy** Dysprosium 66	164.9 **Ho** Holmium 67	167.3 **Er** Erbium 68	168.9 **Tm** Thulium 69	173.0 **Yb** Ytterbium 70	175.0 **Lu** Lutetium 71
232.0 **Th** Thorium 90	(231) **Pa** Protactinium 91	238.1 **U** Uranium 92	(237) **Np** Neptunium 93	(242) **Pu** Plutonium 94	(243) **Am** Americium 95	(247) **Cm** Curium 96	(245) **Bk** Berkelium 97	(251) **Cf** Californium 98	(254) **Es** Einsteinium 99	(253) **Fm** Fermium 100	(256) **Md** Mendeleevium 101	(254) **No** Nobelium 102	(257) **Lr** Lawrencium 103

The Periodic Table and periodicity in the elements of Periods 2 and 3

Module 3

The Periodic Table

Elements are arranged in the Periodic Table:

- in order of their **atomic (proton) number**
- In **groups** having similar physical and chemical properties
- In **periods** showing repeating trends in physical and chemical properties.

The properties of the elements in Period 3 are shown in the table below.

Element	Sodium	Magnesium	Aluminium	Silicon	Phosphorus	Sulfur	Chlorine	Argon
Symbol	Na	Mg	Al	Si	P	S	Cl	Ar
Physical state of element at room temperature	Solid metal	Solid metal	Solid metal	Solid non-metal	Solid non-metal (P_4 molecules)	Solid non-metal (S_8 molecules)	Gas (Cl_2 molecules)	Gas (Ar atoms)
Outer electron configuration	$3s^1$	$3s^2$	$3s^2\,3p^1$	$3s^2\,3p^2$	$3s^2\,3p^3$	$3s^2\,3p^4$	$3s^2\,3p^5$	$3s^2\,3p^6$
Atomic radius /nm	0.191	0.160	0.130	0.118	0.110	0.102	0.099	0.095
Melting point /°C	98	649	660	1410	44	113	−101	−189

Hint

IMPORTANT: A periodic property is one that shows a repeating pattern when plotted against atomic number.

This table shows us trends in the properties of the elements. A trend is a gradually changing event. The trends we see in Period 3 are repeated in all the periods – this regular pattern of trends is called **periodicity**.

Now let's examine the trends across the periods.

Atomic radius

Observation: The atomic radii of the elements decrease across the periods.

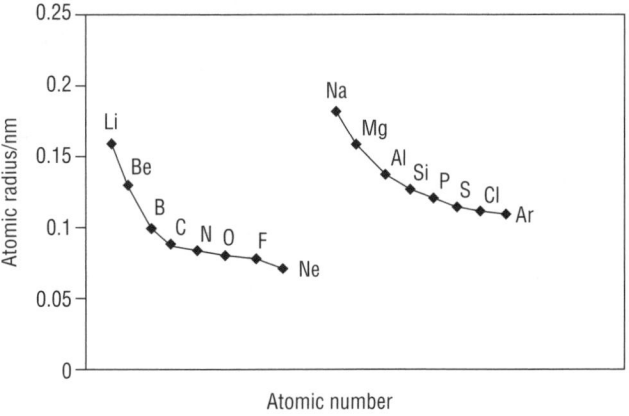

Explanation:

- Across the period, the electrons are added to the same shell and experience similar shielding from the nucleus by inner electrons.

- As the period is crossed from left to right, each successive element gains an extra positively charged proton. This extra positive charge pulls the electrons closer to the nucleus and the atomic radius decreases.

✓ Quick check 2

Ionisation energies

See page 18.

Melting points

Observation: This variation is shown for Li–Ar on the right. For period 3; the melting points rise going across the period to reach a maximum at silicon. Then there is a sharp drop to phosphorus, and then a general decrease to the end of the period.

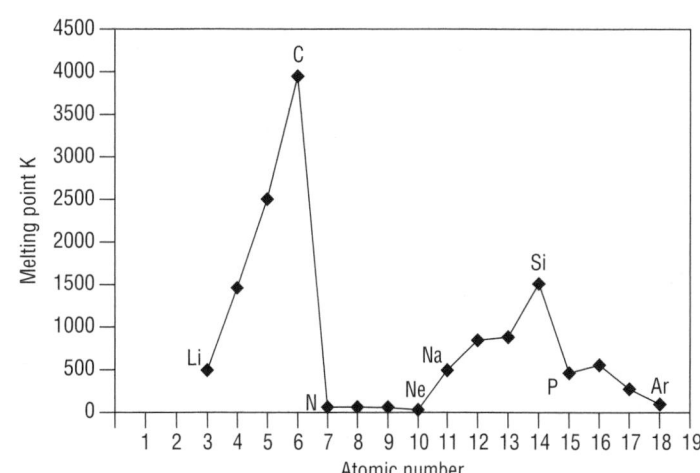

Explanation for Period 3:

The melting points of metals are high, reflecting the strong electrostatic bonding between positive ions and mobile electrons in the metallic bond. The melting points increase from Na → Mg → Al because the number of outer electrons increases and the positive charge on the cations increases from 1 → 2 → 3, so the electrostatic attraction is stronger and the **metallic bond** is more difficult to break.

✓ Quick check 3

- The highest melting point is for silicon, which has a giant covalent structure. **Covalent bonds** are very strong, and require a lot of energy to be broken.

- The simple molecules in phosphorus (P_4) and sulfur (S_8) have weak intermolecular bonds between them, which are easily broken. This means the melting points are much lower than for silicon, although they are solids.

- Finally, Cl_2 and Ar are both gases and have very low melting points because the intermolecular forces between them are even weaker.

✓ Quick check 4

Boiling points follow the same overall trend as melting points.

QUICK CHECK QUESTIONS

1 What term is used to describe the following?
   a A vertical column of elements.
   b A horizontal row of elements.

2 The elements arsenic to krypton are elements in Period 4.
   a Describe how the atomic radius varies from arsenic to krypton.
   b Explain your answer.

3 Sodium, magnesium and aluminium are all metals, but the melting point of sodium is much lower than the others. Explain why this is so.

4 Explain why
   a the melting point of aluminium is lower than that of silicon
   b the melting point of carbon is much higher than that of nitrogen.

Module 3

The Group 2 elements

Key words

- atomic radii
- electrical conductivity

✓ *Quick check 1*

✓ *Quick check 2*

Atomic radius
Mg: 0.160 nm
Ca: 0.174 nm
Sr: 0.191 nm
Ba: 0.198 nm

✓ *Quick check 3*

Trends in the properties of the Group 2 elements magnesium, calcium, strontium and barium are studied in this section. The most important reactions involve **reduction** and **oxidation**.

Physical properties

Electrical conductivities

- All the Group 2 metals are good conductors of electricity because they have metallic bonding, which means positive ions are surrounded by mobile electrons.
- These electrons can move if a potential difference is applied because they are delocalised, so metals are good conductors.

Atomic radii

- The outer electron configurations of the elements are all the same – ns^2, where n is the period number. Mg: $3s^2$, Ca: $4s^2$, Sr: $5s^2$, Ba: $6s^2$
- The atomic radii increase going down the group.
- This is because a new shell of electrons is present with each element, so the size of the atom increases.

Chemical properties

- When the Group 2 elements react, they lose their two outer electrons to form cations with a +2 charge.
- Their reactivity increases down the group because the first and second ionisation energies decrease and it is easier to lose the two outer electrons when they react.
- When they react, they are all oxidised because their oxidation numbers (ON) increase from zero in the element to +2 in the ion.

  E.g. Ca $\rightarrow$ Ca^{2+} + 2e$^-$
  $$0 \qquad +2$$

The reactions of the Group 2 elements with oxygen and water are summarised in the tables below.

Reactions with oxygen		
Element	Reaction	Equation
Magnesium	All tarnish in air and burn when heated. When magnesium is heated in air (oxygen), it burns with a bright white light.	$2Mg(s) + O_2(g) \rightarrow 2MgO(s)$
Calcium		$2Ca(s) + O_2(g) \rightarrow 2CaO(s)$
Strontium		$2Sr(s) + O_2(g) \rightarrow 2SrO(s)$
Barium		$2Ba(s) + O_2(g) \rightarrow 2BaO(s)$

Reactions with water		
Element	Reaction	Equation
Magnesium	Slow reaction with water. Bubbles of hydrogen form slowly over several hours. The solution formed is a weak alkali, $Mg(OH)_2$, with a pH of 9.	$Mg(s) + 2H_2O(l) \rightarrow Mg(OH)_2(aq) + H_2(g)$
Calcium	All these elements react with cold water to form hydrogen gas and an alkaline solution of pH 12 upwards. The speed of the reaction increases as the group is descended.	e.g. $Ca(s) + 2H_2O(l) \rightarrow Ca(OH)_2(aq) + H_2(g)$
Strontium		
Barium		

The thermal decomposition (breaking up by heat) of Group 2 carbonates:

✓ *Quick check 4*

- all Group 2 carbonates decompose when heated to give the metal oxide and carbon dioxide: e.g. $CaCO_3(s) \rightarrow CaO(s) + CO_2(g)$
- it becomes harder to decompose the carbonates as the group is descended, therefore magnesium carbonate is easier to decompose than calcium carbonate, etc.

The use of Group 2 elements and their compounds

Magnesium hydroxide, $Mg(OH)_2$ – this is used in antacids or indigestion remedies. This is because it is a weak alkali, so it neutralises excess stomach acid.

✓ *Quick check 5*

$$Mg(OH)_2 + 2HCl \rightarrow MgCl_2(aq) + 2H_2O(l)$$

Solid calcium hydroxide, $Ca(OH)_2$ – slaked lime – is spread on acidic soil. Slaked lime is basic, so it reduces the acidity of the soil and increases crop yields.

Module 3

QUICK CHECK QUESTIONS

1 Explain why all the Group 2 elements are good electrical conductors.

2 Explain why the size of the Group 2 ions increases as the group is descended.

3 a Explain why beryllium (above Mg in the group) is less reactive than magnesium.
  b i Radium is the bottom element in the group. Predict what would happen if radium (Ra) was added to water. Give an equation for the reaction.
    ii Give the equation for the reaction of radium with oxygen, and explain why the radium is oxidised in the reaction.

4 Give the equation for the thermal decomposition of magnesium carbonate.

5 a How does calcium hydroxide reduce the acidity of soil?
  b Give the equation for the reaction of calcium hydroxide with nitric acid. What type of reaction is this?

The Group 7 elements

The Group 7 elements you will study are chlorine, bromine and iodine. They all have a common outer electron configuration of $ns^2\ np^5$, where n is the principal quantum number.

The Group 7 elements are also called the halogens, and they exist as diatomic molecules Cl_2, Br_2, I_2. They are non-metals. They are very reactive elements.

Physical properties

- As the group is descended, the elements become less volatile. Chlorine is a gas, bromine is a liquid and iodine is a solid. As the group is descended, the number of electrons present in the molecules increases. This leads to an increase in the strength of the **van der Waals' forces** between the molecules.
- The halogens are different colours. Chlorine is a greenish-yellow gas, bromine is a dark red liquid that is volatile and gives off a dark red-brown vapour, and iodine is a shiny grey-black crystalline solid. Iodine sublimes when heated gently – this means it goes straight from the solid to the vapour phase. Iodine vapour is purple.

Chemical properties

- Because the electronic configuration is $ns^2\ np^5$, the halogens have to gain only one more electron to have a full p-orbital. This means that the most common oxidation number for the ions is –1. The ions are called halide ions: Cl^-, Br^-, I^-. Other oxidation states do exist, but they are not common; chlorine in particular can show a range of oxidation numbers from –1 to +7.
- The trend in reactivity is that the halogens become *less reactive* on *descending* the group.

When halogens react, they are reduced to the halide ion, so the substance they react with is oxidised. This means the halogens are *good oxidising agents*. Chlorine is the most powerful oxidising agent of the three and iodine is the least powerful.

Relative reactivities

The relative reactivities (and oxidising powers) of chlorine, bromine and iodine can be shown by displacement reactions.

In a displacement reaction, a more reactive element displaces a less reactive similar element.

$$Cl_2(g) + 2Br^-(aq) \rightarrow 2Cl^-(aq) + Br_2(l)$$

This is a **redox reaction**, where the chlorine acts as an oxidising agent and oxidises the bromide.

The full range of displacement reactions is shown in the table:

	Halogen		
Halide ion	Cl_2	Br_2	I_2
Cl^-		No reaction	No reaction
Br^-	$Cl_2 + 2Br^- \rightarrow Br_2 + 2Cl^-$		No reaction
I^-	$Cl_2 + 2I^- \rightarrow I_2 + 2Cl^-$	$Br_2 + 2I^- \rightarrow I_2 + 2Br^-$	

- These reactions are usually carried out in aqueous solution. But it can be difficult to decide what is happening when you mix together aqueous chlorine and aqueous bromide ion, because the halide ions are all colourless in solution and the halogens have very faint colours (because they do not dissolve in polar water – they are **non-polar molecules**).

- To see what is happening in these displacement reactions, we add cyclohexane. This is a non-polar organic solvent and it dissolves the halogens very well. This means the halogens look coloured in cyclohexane – chlorine is a faint green, bromine is brown-orange, and iodine is purple.

Hint

Cyclohexane is immiscible with water – it floats on top in a separate layer.

✓*Quick check 2*

Module 3

Explanation of the trend in reactivity

- All the Group 7 elements gain an electron when they react to form –1 ions.
- As we descend the group, the atoms increase in size.
- Therefore, as we descend, the electron gained enters an electron **shell** that is further from the nucleus and has greater **electron shielding**.
- Therefore it becomes harder to attract and gain an extra electron and therefore to react.

QUICK CHECK QUESTIONS

1 Explain, in terms of intermolecular forces, why chlorine is a gas but iodine is a solid.
2 State the observations you would make if you mixed bromine water with aqueous sodium iodide and then added cyclohexane. Explain your observations by writing equations to illustrate any reactions that occur.

Reactions of the halogens

Fluorine is the most reactive halogen in the group, because it can capture an electron more easily than the others. That is, fluorine is the strongest **oxidising agent**.

Chlorine, bromine and iodine

Of these three, chlorine is the strongest oxidising agent because it has the smallest atom. The outer p-orbital is closest to the nucleus, so an electron from another atom can easily be transferred and held tightly in the p-orbital. This makes chlorine a strong oxidising agent.

Two important reactions of chlorine are with cold dilute aqueous sodium hydroxide, and with water.

Reaction with aqueous sodium hydroxide

Chlorine reacts with dilute aqueous sodium hydroxide at room temperature to form bleach.

The formula of this bleach is NaClO, and it is called sodium chlorate(I). It is a salt that splits up in water to give free sodium ions and chlorate(I) ions, ClO^-. It is these chlorate(I) ions that have bleaching properties – they oxidise stains and make them colourless.

$$Cl_2(g) + 2NaOH(aq) \rightarrow NaCl(aq) + NaOCl(aq) + H_2O(l)$$

Oxidation number of Cl   0   −1   +1

The ionic equation is $Cl_2 + 2OH^- \rightarrow Cl^- + ClO^- + H_2O$

Oxidation number   0   −1   +1

Look at the oxidation numbers of chlorine in each of the three chlorine-containing species. The element chlorine has an oxidation number of 0, and when it reacts this goes up to +1 in ClO^-, and down to −1 in Cl^-. *The oxidation number of one species is increased and decreased in the same reaction.* Reactions like this are called **disproportionation** reactions.

✔*Quick check 1*

Most domestic bleach is a mixture of aqueous NaCl and NaClO. Stronger commercial bleach is usually HClO, not NaClO. HClO is called hypochlorous acid.

Reaction with water

Chlorine reacts with water to give hydrochloric acid, HCl and hypochlorous [chloric(I) acid], HClO.

✔*Quick check 2*

$$Cl_2(g) + H_2O(l) \rightarrow HCl(aq) + HClO(aq)$$

Oxidation number of Cl   0   −1   +1

This is also a disproportionation reaction – the oxidation number of chlorine increases and decreases in the same reaction.

This reaction is used to purify our water by removing bacteria and making it safe to drink. Water from the reservoir has solid particles removed from it, then it is treated with chlorine. The reaction above shows us that acids are produced, and it is these that kill bacteria. The purified water is then piped to our homes. A small amount of chlorine remains in the water (some people can taste or smell it) to ensure the water remains bacteria-free.

Laboratory test to determine which halide ion is in solution

The halide ions are all colourless in solution, so a simple test is needed to find out which one is present.

STEP 1 Acidify the unknown halide ion solution with nitric acid.

STEP 2 Add silver nitrate solution. A precipitate of the silver halide is formed:
- silver chloride is white
- silver bromide is cream
- silver iodide is yellow.

All three reactions are precipitation reactions; the equations are as follows:

$Ag^+(aq) + Cl^-(aq) \rightarrow AgCl(s)$
$Ag^+(aq) + Br^-(aq) \rightarrow AgBr(s)$
$Ag^+(aq) + I^-(aq) \rightarrow AgI(s)$

STEP 3 It is difficult to decide the colour of the precipitate accurately, so ammonia solution is added:

silver chloride dissolves in *dilute* ammonia solution – the others do not
silver bromide dissolves in *concentrated* ammonia solution
silver iodide *does not dissolve*, even in concentrated ammonia solution.

✓*Quick check 3*

Halide	Addition of silver nitrate solution	Addition of ammonia solution
Cl⁻	**White** precipitate formed	**Soluble** in ammonia solution
Br⁻	**Cream** precipitate formed	**Partially soluble** in ammonia solution
I⁻	**Yellow** precipitate formed	**Insoluble** in ammonia solution

Module 3

QUICK CHECK QUESTIONS

1 Chlorine reacts with concentrated sodium hydroxide solution at 70°C in this way:

$3Cl_2(g) + 6NaOH(aq) \rightarrow 5NaCl(aq) + NaClO_3(aq) + 3H_2O(l)$

  a What is the oxidation state of chlorine in $NaClO_3$?
  b Explain why this is a disproportionation reaction.

2 Identify all the oxidation numbers for chlorine in the ionic equation:

$3ClO^- \rightarrow 2Cl^- + ClO_3^-$.

State and explain which species is oxidised and which is reduced.

3 Write instructions for a trainee analytical chemist who is identifying an unknown halide ion in solution for the first time.

End-of-unit questions

For these questions, you will need the Periodic Table from your data sheet.

1 This question looks at number relationships in Chemistry. The answer to each part is a number.

    a State how many:

        i atoms there are in one molecule of butane (C_4H_{10})   (1)

        ii neutrons there are in an atom of fluorine-19   (1)

        iii protons there are in an oxide ion   (1)

        iv electrons there are in the 3p sub-shell of a sulfur atom.   (1)

    b Determine:

        i how many moles of ions there are in 2 moles of $CaCl_2$ (1)

        ii the oxidation number of vanadium in the VO_3^- ion   (1)

        iii how many electrons there are in an NO_3^- ion   (1)

    c Calculate:

        i the relative atomic mass of naturally occurring gallium, given that naturally occurring gallium has the percentage composition ^{69}Ga, 60%; ^{71}Ga 40%   (1)

        ii how many grams of carbon there are in 8 g of CH_3OH (1)

        iii how many grams of NaOH there are in 500 cm³ of a 0.2 mol dm⁻³ solution   (1)

        [TOTAL 10 marks]

2 Hydrogen fluoride, HF, is one of the most important of fluorine compounds. It can be prepared by reacting calcium fluoride, CaF_2, with sulfuric acid. Calcium sulfate ($CaSO_4$) is the other product.

    a **i** Give the balanced equation for the reaction between calcium fluoride and sulfuric acid.   (1)

        ii What is the volume of hydrogen fluoride gas produced at room temperature and pressure when 7.81 g of calcium fluoride are reacted with excess sulfuric acid? **Show your working**. (1 mol of gas occupies 24 dm³ at room temperature and pressure.)   (2)

    b **i** Showing outer-shell electrons only, draw dot-and-cross diagrams of:

          I hydrogen fluoride   (2)

          II calcium fluoride   (2)

        ii Predict **two** differences between the physical properties of HF and CaF_2. **Explain your answers**.   (2)

    c **i** Draw the s-orbital of hydrogen and a p-orbital from fluorine.   (2)

        ii Give the electron configurations of:

          I a fluorine atom   (1)

          II a Ca^{2+} ion.   (1)

    d Hydrogen fluoride and water both have higher than expected boiling points because of hydrogen bonding between their molecules.

        i Draw a diagram showing the hydrogen bonding between water molecules.   (3)

        ii Water and methane (CH_4) have almost identical relative molecular masses. Explain why water has a boiling point of 100°C while that of methane is −164°C.   (2)

    e In aqueous solution, hydrogen fluoride (like HCl) is acidic. Explain why this is.   (1)

f i Give the balanced symbol equation for the reaction of an aqueous solution of HF with calcium carbonate. (1)

ii Give and explain one observation for this reaction. (1)

[TOTAL 21 marks]

3 Wines often contain a small amount of sulfur dioxide that is added as a preservative. The amount of sulfur dioxide added needs to be calculated carefully: too little, and the wine readily goes bad; too much, and the wine tastes of sulfur dioxide. The sulfur dioxide content of a wine can be found by using its reaction with aqueous iodine:

$$SO_2(aq) + I_2(aq) + 2H_2O(l) \rightarrow SO_4^{2-}(aq) + 2I^-(aq) + 4H^+(aq)$$

a State the oxidation number of sulfur in SO_2 and in SO_4^{2-}. (2)

b Explain why the reaction between sulfur dioxide and iodine is a redox reaction. (2)

c The sulfur dioxide content of a wine can be found by titration. An analyst found that the sulfur dioxide in $50.0\,cm^3$ of a sample of white wine reacted with exactly $16.4\,cm^3$ of $0.0100\,mol\,dm^{-3}$ aqueous iodine.
How many moles of:

i iodine (I_2) did the analyst use in the titration? (1)

ii sulfur dioxide were in the $50.0\,cm^3$ of wine? (1)

iii What was the concentration (in $mol\,dm^{-3}$) of sulfur dioxide in the wine? (1)

iv What was the concentration (in $g\,dm^{-3}$) of sulfur dioxide in the wine? (2)

[TOTAL 9 marks]

4 The graph below shows the variation in first ionisation energy (IE) with atomic number for the second and third periods of the Periodic Table.

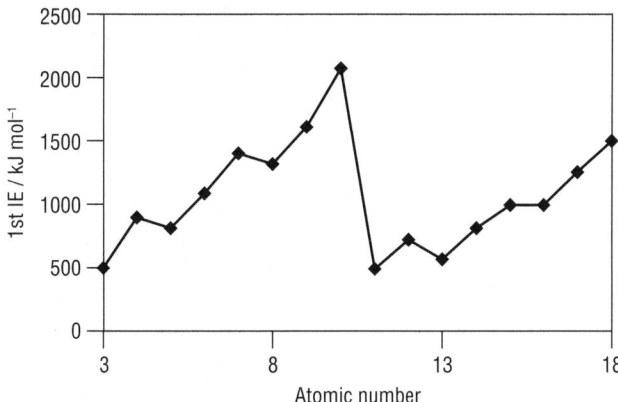

a Define the term first ionisation energy. (3)

b Explain why first ionisation energy is a periodic property. (1)

c Explain the overall trend for first ionisation energy across a period. (2)

d Explain why the first ionisation energy of sodium is less than that of lithium. (2)

e The variation in atomic radius is another periodic property. Describe how it changes across a period, and explain this variation. (2)

[TOTAL 10 MARKS]

OVERALL 50 MARKS

UNIT 2 (F322)

Chains, Energy and Resources

Modules 1 and 2 – Basic concepts and hydrocarbons, alcohols, halogenoalkanes and analysis, pages 44–71

These modules deal with the basics of naming, formulae and isomerism and the chemistry of the homologous series of alkanes, alkenes, halogenoalkanes and alcohols. The chemistry of crude oil, fuels and addition polymerisation is dealt with separately.

The table below summarises the content and the previous knowledge and understanding required for efficient revision of the topics. For example, before reading the alkanes section, it would be a good idea to look at the naming and isomers section first. You will also need to refer to the Atoms, Bonds and Groups unit, where intermolecular forces are covered. The table below refers you to the main sections and where previous knowledge is necessary.

Summary

Topic (in this book)	Reference to specification	Ideas from GCSE
Basic concepts – formulae and isomerism	2.1.1	You should already have looked at formulae in Unit 1, but the terms structural and displayed formulae are most used in this module.
Basic concepts – naming	2.1.1	Most of this is new material.
Basic concepts – percentage yields and atom economy	2.1.1	From Unit 1 – moles and reacting masses.
The alkanes and cycloalkanes	2.1.2	From Unit 1 – covalent bonding and shapes of molecules. Intermolecular forces – Van der Waals' forces
Hydrocarbons as fuels	2.1.2	This follows on from the alkanes. Fractional distillation and cracking. There is a lot of new material here.
The alkenes	2.1.3	Hydrocarbons and formulae. From Unit 1 – bonding and molecular shapes.
Reactions of the alkenes	2.1.3	From Unit 1 – polarised bonds.
Addition polymerisation	2.1.3	You will need a good understanding of the alkenes section.
The alcohols	2.2.1	From Unit 1 – hydrogen bonding.
Types of alcohol	2.2.1	From Unit 1 – oxidation.
The halogenoalkanes	2.2.2	The identity of the halogens. The naming of these compounds should be understood.
Modern analytical techniques (infrared and mass spectroscopy)	2.2.3	All this is new, but you should have a good knowledge of the structure of functional groups studied previously in this unit.
Questions		These questions will test you on this part of the unit.

Modules 3 and 4 – Energy and resources, pages 72–85

Module 3 deals with physical chemistry, notably energy, rates of reaction and equilibrium. As above, you will be building on some previous knowledge, but most of this material is from your new lessons in AS Chemistry. Module 4 looks at our environment and our effects on it

Topic (in this book)	Reference to specification	Ideas from GCSE
Energy	2.3.1	A lot of this material is new, but you will have done some work on exothermic and endothermic heat changes. Your knowledge of covalent bonding from Unit 1 will also be useful here. Review your knowledge of moles and rearranging equations.
Rates of reaction	2.3.2	You should review collision theory and your knowledge of the effects of concentration, surface area and temperature on reaction rates.
Chemical equilibria	2.3.2	What you have learned in the energy section will be useful here, but most of this content will be new.
Chemistry of the air – the greenhouse effect	2.4.1	You will have some previous knowledge of this topic. Some knowledge of the basic physics of the electromagnetic spectrum will be useful.
Atmospheric pollution	2.4.1	As with the greenhouse effect, you will have come across the problems associated with depletion of the ozone layer, but you will need to review work on radical substitution and catalysis. Review your work on catalysts and combustion of alkanes and other hydrocarbons.
Green chemistry	2.4.2	Review previous work on atom economy

End-of-unit questions, pages 86–88

UNIT 2

Formulae and isomerism

This important section deals with two basics of organic chemistry – types of formulae and the isomerism of organic compounds. You should know about empirical and molecular formulae as covered in the first unit, Atoms, bonds and groups. Skeletal formulae are an important, alternative way of showing the structures of carbon compounds.

Key words

- empirical
- molecular
- structural
- isomerism
- displayed
- skeletal
- stereoisomerism
- *E/Z* isomerism

Types of formulae

- The **empirical formula** is the simplest whole-number ratio of the number of atoms of each element in a compound. For example, all alkenes with one double bond have the empirical formula CH_2. The molecular formulae for ethene (C_2H_4) and propene (C_3H_6) can be simplified to CH_2.

- A **molecular formula** gives the actual number of atoms of each element present in a molecule. For example, $C_4H_{10}O$ is the molecular formula of the alcohol butan-1-ol with four carbon atoms, 10 hydrogen atoms and one oxygen atom.

- A **general formula** is the simplest algebraic formula to represent any member of a homologous series. For example, any alkane with n carbons has the formula C_nH_{2n+2}.

- A **structural formula** gives minimal detail to show how the atoms are arranged in the molecule. For example, butanol, $C_4H_{10}O$, can exist in four different forms (structural isomers), all with the same molecular formula but with different arrangements of the atoms. See below for more details on structural isomerism.

$CH_3CH_2CH_2CH_2OH$	$CH_3CH_2CH(OH)CH_3$	$(CH_3)_2CHCH_2OH$	$(CH_3)_3COH$
butan-1-ol	butan-2-ol	2-methylpropan-1-ol	2-methylpropan-2-ol

- A **displayed formula** gives the most accurate representation of the molecule, showing all the atoms and bonds present, and can give some indication of the relative positions of the atoms in space. For example, propene can be represented as shown in the margin rather than as $CH_3CH=CH_2$.

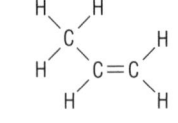

✓ *Quick check 1, 3, 4*

- A **skeletal formula** is a simplified organic formula with carbon atoms shown as a skeleton and all the hydrogen atoms of the alkyl chains removed except for those of **functional groups**. For example, the four structural isomers of butanol can be represented as shown below:

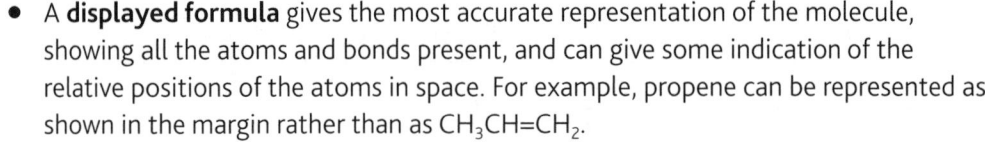

Isomerism

There are two different types of isomerism.

- In **structural isomerism** the structural arrangements of atoms are different. The carbon chain may be different, or the functional group and/or its position in the molecule may be different. Structural isomers of a compound have the same molecular formulae, but have different structural and displayed formulae.

✓ *Quick check 2*

- In **stereoisomerism** the structural formulae are identical but the displayed formulae are different because the isomers have different arrangements of the atoms in space. There are two types, *E/Z* isomers (see 'The alkenes', page 54) and optical isomers (this is part of the A2 specification and is not required for AS level).

✓ *Quick check 4*

■ WORKED EXAMPLE

What are the structural and stereoisomers of the alkene with the molecular formula C_4H_8?

Answer: There are three isomers with different structural formulae:

$$CH_3CH_2CH=CH_2 \qquad CH_3CH=CHCH_3 \qquad (CH_3)_2C=CH_2$$

Also, the middle isomer can have 2 *E/Z* stereoisomers:

![displayed formulae of E-isomer and Z-isomer]

E-isomer   *Z*-isomer

Some more examples of structural isomers are given below.

Molecular formula	Structural isomers	
C_4H_{10}	$CH_3CH_2CH_2CH_3$ $CH_3CH(CH_3)CH_3$	butane 2-methylpropane
C_3H_7Cl	$CH_3CH_2CH_2Cl$ $CH_3CHClCH_3$	1-chloropropane 2-chloropropane
C_4H_9OH	$CH_3CH_2CH_2CH_2OH$ $CH_3CH_2CH(OH)CH_3$ $(CH_3)_3COH$ $(CH_3)_2CHCH_2OH$	butan-1-ol butan-2-ol 2-methylpropan-2-ol 2-methylpropan-1-ol

QUICK CHECK QUESTIONS

1 Draw the displayed formulae of the isomers of the following compounds:
   a C_5H_{12}
   b C_3H_7OH (only those isomers with an –OH group).
2 Give the skeletal formulae of the isomers of C_5H_{12}.
3 Draw the displayed formulae for as many isomers as you can of the following compounds:
   a $C_2H_4Cl_2$
   b C_6H_{14}.
4 C_5H_{10} has six alkene isomers. Two of them are *E/Z* isomers (see 'The alkenes', page 54). Draw the displayed formulae for all six isomers.

Naming organic compounds

Key words

- alkanes
- functional groups
- halogenoalkanes
- alkenes
- alcohols

Naming organic compounds using their formulae, or constructing their structural and displayed formulae from their names, is an important part of organic chemistry. The names used in this unit are based on the International Union of Pure and Applied Chemistry (IUPAC) convention. We will look at the naming of all the groups of compounds found on your AS specification.

Naming alkanes

- Their names always end in the suffix -ane.
- The first 10 alkanes are listed in the table opposite.
- Alkyl groups are named according to the alkane from which they are derived. For example, the CH_3- group is derived from methane and is called the methyl group. Similarly, C_2H_5- comes from ethane and is called the ethyl group.

Number of carbons	Name
1	Methane
2	Ethane
3	Propane
4	Butane
5	Pentane
6	Hexane
7	Heptane
8	Octane
9	Nonane
10	Decane

How is it done?

■ **WORKED EXAMPLE**

$$H-\underset{\underset{H}{|}}{\overset{\overset{H}{|}}{C}}-\underset{\underset{CH_3}{|}}{\overset{\overset{H}{|}}{C}}-\underset{\underset{H}{|}}{\overset{\overset{H}{|}}{C}}-\underset{\underset{H}{|}}{\overset{\overset{H}{|}}{C}}-H$$

The steps in naming this alkane are as follows:

STEP 1 Identify the longest carbon chain. In this case it is four carbons. Therefore the parent compound is butane.

STEP 2 Number the carbon (the lowest possible number) to which the alkyl substituent group is attached. Here it is the second carbon, so the alkyl group is indicated by the prefix 2-methyl. If there is more than one alkyl group, the numbers of carbon atoms to which they are attached are indicated in the formula.

STEP 3 Put the two parts together and name the whole compound – in this case, 2-methylbutane.

Examples are given in the table.

Structural formula	Longest carbon chain	Identity and position of alkyl group	Name
$CH_3CH(CH_3)CH_3$	3	Methyl group on second carbon	2-methylpropane
$CH_3C(CH_3)_2CH_3$	3	Two methyl groups on second carbon	2,2-dimethylpropane
$CH_3CH(CH_3)CH_2CH_3$	4	Methyl group on second carbon	2-methylbutane

Functional groups

A functional group is a group of atoms found in a compound that are responsible for the characteristic reactions of the compound. Examples of functional groups you will meet are shown in the table below.

Group of compounds	Functional group present
Alkenes	$\diagdown$C=C$\diagup$ bond
Halogenoalkanes	C–halogen bond, e.g. C–Cl
Alcohols	–OH
Carboxylic acids	–COOH

Naming halogenoalkanes

STEP 1 Find the longest carbon chain.
STEP 2 Put the position (lowest number possible) and name of the halogen in front. The halogen is always halo-, e.g. bromine is bromo-.

✔ *Quick check 1, 2, 3*

Examples are given in the table.

Structural formula	Longest carbon chain	Identity and position of halogen atom	Name
$CH_3CH_2CHICH_3$	4	Iodine on second	2-iodobutane
$CH_3CH_2CH_2Br$	3	Bromine on first	1-bromopropane
$CH_3CH(CH_3)CH_2Cl$	3	Chlorine on first	1-chloro-2-methylpropane

Naming alkenes

STEP 1 Find the longest carbon chain and change the ending from -ane to -ene.
STEP 2 The lowest possible number for the C=C bond position is indicated by the number in the name (unless there is only one possibility).

✔ *Quick check 1 and 3*

Examples are given in the table.

Structural formula	Longest carbon chain	Position of double bond	Name
$CH_3CH=CH_2$	3	First carbon	Propene
$CH_3CH_2CH=CH_2$	4	First carbon	But-1-ene
$CH_3CH_2CH=CHCH_3$	5	Second carbon	Pent-2-ene

Naming alcohols

STEP 1 Find the longest carbon chain and name the alkane (without the -e).
STEP 2 The lowest position of the –OH group is indicated by a number followed by -ol.

✔ *Quick check 1, 2, 4*

Examples are given in the table.

Structural formula	Longest carbon chain	Position of –OH group	Name
$CH_3CH(OH)CH_3$	3	Second carbon	Propan-2-ol
$CH_3CH_2CH_2CH_2OH$	4	First carbon	Butan-1-ol
$CH_3CH(CH_3)CH_2OH$	5	First carbon	2-methylpropan-1-ol

QUICK CHECK QUESTIONS

1 Name the following compounds:
   a $CH_3CH_2CH(OH)CH_3$ **b** $CH_3CH_2CH_2Cl$
   c $CH_3CH=CHCH_3$ **d** $CH_3CHBrCH_3$

2 Draw the displayed formulae of the following compounds:
   a 2-chlorobutane;   **b** propan-1-ol;
   c 2-methylpropan-2-ol;   **d** 2-chloropropene

3 Why is it that for bromoethane and propene no numbers are required to indicate the positions of the halogen atom or double bond?

4 Draw and name the *four* structural isomers of the alcohols with the formula C_4H_9OH.

Percentage yield and atom economy

Percentage yield

- All organic chemists need to know the efficiency of their preparations. The most frequent question asked in this area of the specification is: 'What is the percentage yield?'

- Put simply, the percentage yield may be expressed as:

$$\text{percentage yield} = \left(\frac{\text{actual yield}}{\text{theoretical yield}}\right) \times 100\%$$

Or:

$$\text{percentage yield} = \left(\frac{\text{what you get}}{\text{what you should get}}\right) \times 100\%$$

■ WORKED EXAMPLE

Bromoethane can be prepared by reacting excess hydrogen bromide (from the reaction between NaBr and concentrated H_2SO_4) with ethanol. The mixture is heated and the bromoethane is distilled off.

When 9.20 g of ethanol ($M_r = 46.0$) is reacted with excess hydrogen bromide, 13.08 g of bromoethane ($M_r = 108.9$) are formed. What is the percentage yield?

STEP 1 We have to find out what we should get (our theoretical yield). First we have to construct the equation for the reaction:

$$HBr + C_2H_5OH \rightarrow C_2H_5Br + H_2O$$

STEP 2 Calculate the number of moles of ethanol in the reaction:

$$\text{number of moles} = \frac{\text{mass}}{M} = \frac{9.20}{46.0} = 0.200 \text{ mol}$$

STEP 3 From the equation, in this reaction 1 mol of ethanol gives 1 mol of bromoethane, therefore 0.200 mol *should* give 0.200 mol of bromoethane.

STEP 4 Calculate the mass of bromoethane we should get:

$$\text{mass of bromoethane} = \text{amount (mol)} \times M = 0.2.00 \times 108.9 = 21.78 \text{ g}$$

STEP 5 Calculate the percentage yield:

$$\left(\frac{\text{what you get}}{\text{what you should get}}\right) \times 100\% = \left(\frac{13.08}{21.78}\right) \times 100\% = 60.1\%$$

Another question you might be asked about yields is: 'Suggest why the percentage yield is substantially below 100%.'

The *wrong* answer to this question is anything suggesting human error.

Examples of wrong answers

1 The student weighed it out incorrectly.
2 The student dropped some of it.

Your answers to this type of question should describe something about the reaction.

Examples

1 When distilling, not all the distillate was evaporated from the mixture.
2 When recrystallising, not all the crystals crystallised from solution.
3 The reaction did not go to completion.
4 The receiver was not cooled, therefore not all the distillate condensed.

Atom economy

Apart from wanting a good yield from their preparations, chemists have to take into account the environment, and the waste when unwanted chemicals are produced during chemical reactions. A measure of the amount of starting materials that end up as the product you want is the **atom economy** of a reaction.

✓*Quick check 3*

The atom economy of a reaction can be defined as follows:

$$\text{atom economy} = \frac{\text{molecular mass of desired product}}{\text{sum of molecular masses of all products}} \times 100\%$$

✓*Quick check 2*

- Some chemical reactions will theoretically have an atom economy of 100%; others will never reach 100%.

- If we assume our preparation techniques are faultless and our yields will be 100%, addition reactions will theoretically have an atom economy of 100%.

- Substitution reactions will always have an atom economy of less than 100%.

Example 1

The reaction between ethene ($M_r = 28.0$) and bromine ($M_r = 159.8$) is an addition reaction. The desired product is 1,2-dibromoethane ($M_r = 187.8$) – this is the *only* product.

$$C_2H_4(g) + Br_2(l) \rightarrow C_2H_4Br_2(l)$$

Therefore the atom economy of the reaction is:

$$\frac{\text{molecular mass of 1,2-dibromoethane}}{\text{combined molecular mass of all products}} \times 100\%$$

$$= 187.8/187.8 \times 100\%$$
$$= 100\%$$

Example 2

The reaction between ethanol ($M_r = 46.0$) and hydrogen bromide ($M_r = 80.1$) produces the unwanted product water ($M_r = 18.0$) and the desired product bromoethane ($M_r = 108.9$).

Therefore the atom economy of the reaction is:

$$\frac{\text{molecular mass of bromoethane}}{\text{combined molecular mass of all products}} \times 100\%$$

$$= 108.9/126.9 \times 100\%$$
$$= 85.8\%$$

QUICK CHECK QUESTIONS

1 In the preparation of bromoethane, ethanol (CH_3CH_2OH) is reacted with HBr according to the following equation:

$$CH_3CH_2OH + HBr \rightarrow CH_3CH_2Br + H_2O$$

In one such preparation, 9.2 g of ethanol gave 5.36 g of bromoethane. What is the percentage yield?

2 Propan-1-ol ($CH_3CH_2CH_2OH$) can be prepared by a number of methods. Two of them are described by the equations below:

A $CH_3CH_2CH_2Br + KOH \rightarrow CH_3CH_2CH_2OH + KBr$

B $CH_3CH=CH_2 + H_2O \rightarrow CH_3CH_2CH_2OH$

a Calculate the atom economy for both methods. Show your working.
b Which method is better to use? Explain your reasoning.

3 Why do some chemists believe that atom economy is a better way than percentage yield to assess the efficiency of a chemical method?

The alkanes and cycloalkanes

Key words

- homologous series
- hydrocarbon
- saturated
- combustion
- radical
- substitution
- initiation
- propagation
- termination
- homolytic fission

✓*Quick check 1*

Background

- Hydrocarbons are compounds of hydrogen and carbon *only*.
- The alkanes are a **homologous series** of **hydrocarbons**, therefore the members of the series have the same general formula (C_nH_{2n+2}). For example, in ethane $n=2$, so there are $2 \times 2+2=6$ hydrogens, molecular formula C_2H_6.
- Cycloalkanes have the general formula C_nH_{2n}, where n must be 3 or above.
- As with all homologous series, the formulae of successive members of the series differ by $-CH_2$.
- Alkanes and cycloalkanes have no multiple bonds in their molecules and are therefore **saturated hydrocarbons**.
- All the bond angles are 109.5° and each carbon atom is the centre of a tetrahedron with other atoms at each of the four corners. This shape gives the maximum separation of bond-pair electrons.
- The only bonds present in the molecules are either C–C or C–H bonds. These bonds are non-polar, making alkanes and cycloalkanes unreactive – they have few reactions.
- Because they are non-polar molecules, the forces between molecules are weak **van der Waals' forces**.
- Their main uses are as fuels and feedstock for the production of other chemicals. For example, methane is the main constituent of natural gas, and is burned to produce heat. It is also used in the Haber process to make hydrogen for production of ammonia.
- Longer-chain alkanes are **cracked** to give alkenes and shorter alkanes that are used as fuels.

Hint

These forces increase with increasing length of carbon chain.

Combustion

- All alkanes undergo complete combustion (burn in excess air containing oxygen) to give carbon dioxide and water.

  e.g. $CH_4(g) + 2O_2(g) \rightarrow CO_2(g) + 2H_2O(l)$

- If there is poor ventilation, the lack of oxygen causes incomplete combustion, and poisonous carbon monoxide is formed along with water.

  e.g. $CH_4(g) + 1\frac{1}{2}O_2(g) \rightarrow CO(g) + 2H_2O(l)$

✓*Quick check 2*

- There are several pollutants in the exhaust fumes from combustion in car engines. These are removed using a catalytic converter (see page 84). This is a palladium–platinum–rhodium **catalyst** on a ceramic honeycomb, with a large surface area. The catalyst changes the pollutants to harmless products, as shown in the table.

Pollutant	How is it formed?	What is it converted to?
Hydrocarbons	Unburned fuel	CO_2 and H_2O
Carbon monoxide	Incomplete combustion of hydrocarbons	CO_2
Oxides of nitrogen (NO$_x$)	Reaction between oxygen and nitrogen in the air in a car engine	CO_2 and nitrogen

Melting and boiling points of alkanes

✓*Quick check 3*

- The longer the carbon chain, the greater the surface area of the molecule that can take part in intermolecular bonding, and the greater the van der Waals' forces.
- When the alkanes are branched, the surface area is less, and consequently the van der Waals' forces are weaker.

Radical substitution

In this reaction, a hydrogen on the alkane is replaced (substituted) by chlorine or bromine. The overall reaction for methane is:

$$CH_4(g) + Cl_2(g) \rightarrow CH_3Cl(l) + HCl(g)$$

The product is a halogenoalkane.

There are three stages in this reaction mechanism:

Initiation

$$Cl_2 \rightarrow 2Cl\bullet$$

The radicals are produced at this stage (• on the chlorine indicates a radical – a chlorine atom with an unpaired electron). It always involves breaking of the Cl–Cl covalent bond by UV radiation. Because two radicals are formed by the splitting, this is called **homolytic fission**.

Hint

The word **homolytic** means to break down (*lysis*) into the same (*homo*). **Fission** means to split.

Propagation

This stage keeps the reaction going because it produces radicals, making it into a chain reaction. Examples of reactions at this stage are:

$$CH_4 + Cl\bullet \rightarrow CH_3\bullet + HCl$$

($CH_3\bullet$ is a methyl radical – a methyl group with an unpaired electron.)

$$CH_3\bullet + Cl_2 \rightarrow CH_3Cl + Cl\bullet$$

✓*Quick check 4*

Termination

This ends the chain reaction because radicals are 'mopped up'.

$$CH_3\bullet + CH_3\bullet \rightarrow C_2H_6 \text{ (ethane)}$$
$$CH_3\bullet + Cl\bullet \rightarrow CH_3Cl \text{ (chloromethane)}$$
$$Cl\bullet + Cl\bullet \rightarrow Cl_2$$

The products of chain reactions are difficult to predict because the reactions are difficult to control. For example, CH_2Cl_2 may be formed as the substitution proceeds further.

QUICK CHECK QUESTIONS

1 Give the molecular formula for octane, the alkane with eight carbons.
2 Write a balanced symbol equation for the following:
   a the complete combustion of propane
   b the incomplete combustion of propane.
3 Butane can form two structural isomers.
   a Draw their displayed formulae and name them.
   b Which structural isomer has the higher boiling point?
   c Explain your answer to **b**.
4 One of the products of the radical substitution of methane by chlorine is C_2H_6. Explain how you think this might have been formed.

UNIT
2

Hydrocarbons as fuels

Key words

- fuel
- non-renewable
- fractionation
- knocking
- octane rating
- biofuels
- additive

✓ *Quick check 1*

Crude oil is a source of important chemicals and fuels, and several processes are used to carry out the changes involved. Here we consider the hydrocarbons obtained from fossil fuels. You will have learned about burning and hydrocarbons at GCSE.

What is a good fuel?

Petrol (a mixture of readily available, low-boiling-point **hydrocarbons**) is an example of a good fuel. There are several reasons why:

- its vapour mixes easily with air/oxygen and ignites at low temperature
- as a liquid, it is easily transported and easy to store
- it leaves little or no residue after it has burned
- when it burns, it releases large amounts of energy and large volumes of gases that can drive a car piston
- the structures of the hydrocarbons in the petrol mixture can be changed so that they burn steadily and smoothly.

Facts about crude oil and other fossil fuels

- The three main fossil fuels are coal, oil and natural gas.
- They were formed over millions of years and cannot be replaced, and are therefore **non-renewable**.
- They are also valuable sources of other important chemicals, which are useful either themselves or as starting materials (feedstock) in other chemical processes. Methane, for example, is used in the Haber process for making hydrogen.
- Crude oil is mostly a mixture of alkanes with different boiling points.

Processes used in the petroleum industry

Fractional distillation

- This separates the components of crude oil on a fractionating column, on the basis of their different boiling points.
- The heavier fractions, with high boiling points, condense first and therefore come off lower down the column; lighter fractions come off higher up.

Cracking

- We obtain only 20% of the petrol required for transport from fractional distillation. Therefore another process is needed to make up the shortfall.
- Cracking uses a high temperature and a catalyst to break up longer-chain alkane molecules into alkenes (used in polymerisation) and either more useful shorter alkanes (used as fuels) or hydrogen. It is a type of thermal decomposition.

Hint

Equations for cracking are easily balanced if you know the products. Alkanes have the general formula C_nH_{2n+2}; alkenes have the general formula C_nH_{2n}.

Examples:

$$C_{10}H_{22}(l) \rightarrow C_8H_{18}(l) + C_2H_4(g)$$

$$C_4H_{10}(g) \rightarrow C_4H_8(g) + H_2(g)$$

Knocking and octane ratings

- In a car engine, straight-chain alkanes ignite prematurely, causing 'knocking', which can damage the engine. They have low octane numbers.
- If the molecule is branched, less knocking occurs.
- One way to improve the efficiency of fuel is for straight-chain alkanes to be converted into branched-chain and cyclic molecules and added to petrol.

One process uses a catalyst to convert straight-chain into branched-chain alkanes.

Example:

$$CH_3(CH_2)_6CH_3 \rightarrow CH_3CH(CH_3)CH_2C(CH_3)_2CH_3$$

octane   → 2,2,4-trimethylpentane

Another way to increase the octane rating is to convert the straight-chain alkane into a cycloalkane.

- This process needs a catalyst and a moderately high temperature.
- The straight-chain alkane loses hydrogen to form a cycloalkane:

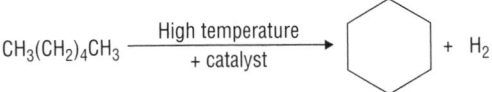

Alternative fuels

Because of the need to conserve fossil fuels, alternative fuels are now being used in greater quantities.

Examples

- Biogas is fuel made from the anaerobic digestion of waste material, such as animal manure and dead plants. Its main constituent is methane.
- Biodiesel is produced from vegetable oils, and is a substitute for diesel. For example, waste vegetable oil from chip-fryers can be used for heating.
- Alcohols such as ethanol can be made from wheat, corn and sugar.

Module 1

> **Hint**
>
> The higher the octane number, the less the amount of knocking. Octane numbers range from 0 for heptane to 100 for 2,2,4-trimethylpentane (these are used as standards). Other examples are n-octane, with a value of –20, and benzene, 120.

> ✓ *Quick check 2 and 3*

> **Hint**
>
> The structures for cycloalkanes are usually represented using skeletal formulae.

QUICK CHECK QUESTIONS

1   Write the equation for the complete combustion of heptane (C_7H_{16}) and explain why the reaction causes the volume to increase.

2   Octane (C_8H_{18}) from crude oil can be converted into 2,2,4-trimethylpentane and 1,4-dimethylcyclohexane, $C_6H_{10}(CH_3)_2$.
   a   Describe the processes used to carry out these conversions.
   b   Give the equations for the reactions taking place.

3   a   Write equations for the cracking of dodecane ($C_{12}H_{26}$) into:
      i   decane ($C_{10}H_{22}$) and ethene
      ii   octane and butene.
   b   Decane and octane are straight-chain compounds. Why are they not used in this form as fuels in the car engine?
   c   Give the skeletal formulae for the following:
      i   a branched-chain compound formed from hexane with a longest chain of four carbons
      ii   a cycloalkane formed from octane.

The alkenes

The alkenes are an extremely important **homologous series**. Their reactions give you a good insight into reaction mechanisms. They are the building blocks for the manufacture of polymers and plastics.

Background facts

- The alkenes are a homologous series of **hydrocarbons**. The **functional group** is the C=C in their molecules. Each member of the series differs from the next by CH_2.

- Because the C=C bond is a multiple bond, they are unsaturated compounds. Their reactions are characteristic of this functional group.

- Their general formula is C_nH_{2n}. For example, ethene has two carbons and therefore four hydrogens.

- The C=C bond consists of a σ (sigma) bond and a π (pi) bond (see below).

✓*Quick check 1*

- They undergo **addition reactions** in which the alkene reacts with another compound to form a single product molecule.

For example:

$$H_2C{=}CH_2(g) \ + \ Br_2(l) \ \rightarrow \ BrCH_2{-}CH_2Br(l)$$
$$\text{ethene} \qquad \text{bromine} \qquad \text{1,2-dibromoethane}$$

- In addition, alkenes react with electron-pair acceptors called **electrophiles**. Examples of electrophiles are polarised Br_2 or H in HBr (or HCl).

- The best test for an alkene is the reaction with bromine water in the dark. The bromine changes from orange to colourless as an addition product is formed. For example, propene reacts as follows to form 1,2-dibromopropane – a dihalogenoalkane:

$$CH_3CH{=}CH_2(g) \ + \ Br_2(aq) \ \rightarrow \qquad CH_3CH(Br){-}CH_2Br$$
$$\text{colourless gas} \qquad \text{orange} \qquad \text{colourless addition product}$$

- Alkenes exhibit *E/Z* isomerism, a type of **stereoisomerism**. For example, but-2-ene has two isomers, an *E* and a *Z* isomer (see below).

- Their main use is in the production of **addition polymers**. For example, ethene forms polyethene; propene forms polypropene (see page 58).

Shape and bonding

✓*Quick check 2*

- The σ-bond lies along the line (axis) between the C=C carbons.

- The π-bond lies above and below the plane of the flat alkene molecule.

- The π-electrons do not contribute to the shape. Round each carbon atom there are three pairs of σ-electrons, therefore the shape around each one is trigonal (triangular) planar.

- The bond angles are 120°.

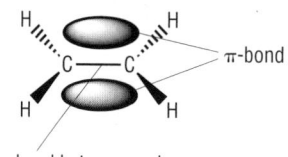

σ-bond between carbons

E/Z isomerism

✓ *Quick check 3 and 4*

Module 1

- Compounds with the same structural formula, but with different positions of their atoms in space, are called stereoisomers. This type of isomerism is called stereoisomerism.

- In alkenes there is no free rotation about the C=C bond, therefore the groups attached to the carbons on the C=C bond are in fixed positions.

Hint

Z stands for *zusammen* (German for together); *E* stands for *entgegen* (opposite).

- If the atoms or groups on each carbon atom of the C=C bond are different, stereoisomers can exist. This type of stereoisomerism is called *E/Z* isomerism.

- The atoms/groups at each end of the C=C bond are assigned priority numbers. For example, a CH_3– group has a higher priority than an H– atom.

- If the high-priority groups are on different carbons but on the same side of the C=C bond, it is the *Z*-isomer. If they are diagonally opposite then it is the *E*-isomer.

- *cis–trans* isomerism is a special case of *E/Z* isomerism where there are two hydrogen atoms and two non-hydrogen groups around the double bond. In this special case, the *Z* isomer is termed *cis*- and the *E* isomer is termed *trans*-.

Example: but-2-ene

Structural formula	$CH_3CH=CHCH_3$	$CH_3CH=CHCH_3$
Displayed formula	![displayed formula: H and CH₃ on C=C with H₃C and H]	![displayed formula: H₃C and CH₃ on C=C with H and H]
Positions of groups	Groups on the opposite sides	Groups on the same side
E/Z naming	*E*-but-2-ene	*Z*-but-2-ene
cis–trans naming	*trans*-but-2-ene	*cis*-but-2-ene

QUICK CHECK QUESTIONS

1. Draw the displayed formulae for the four isomers of butene (C_4H_8).
2. Explain why the bond angles in ethene and other alkenes are 120°.
3. a What type of isomerism is shown by alkenes but not by alkanes?
   b Explain why this is a form of stereoisomerism, not structural isomerism.
   c Which of the following compounds show this form of stereoisomerism? Explain your answers.
      i $(CH_3)_2C=CH_2$
      ii $CH_3CH_2CH=CHCH_3$
4. The following substituted alkenes show *E/Z* isomerism. For each one, draw and name the *E/Z* isomers:
   a $C_2H_2Cl_2$ b $C_4H_6Br_2$

Reactions of the alkenes

Key words

- addition
- unsymmetrical
- symmetrical
- polymer

✓*Quick check 3*

Hint

In this reaction, the electron-deficient bromine accepts a pair of electrons and therefore acts as an electrophile.

- The π-bond (see page 54) produces two regions of high electron density in the molecule. In reactions, this attracts positive ions or δ+ atoms, or even induces dipoles in some molecules (e.g. Br_2).

- When alkenes react, the electrons in the π-bond form a covalent bond with the more positive part of the attacking molecule. The mechanism for bromine is shown below.

- Because the alkene adds to an electrophile, the mechanism is called an electrophilic addition.

The mechanism below shows the sequence of reactions for an alkene and bromine. The curly arrows mean that a pair of electrons is on the move.

The Br–Br bond is polarised as it approaches the high electron density on the C=C bond

The electrons on the C=C move out to form a dative covalent bond and *heterolytic fission* of the Br–Br bond takes place

The *carbocation* (positive carbon) is then attacked by the negative Br⁻ ion

The product is a saturated compound

- In these addition reactions, two molecules add together to form one larger molecule.

- You should think of these addition reactions as reactions with X–Y adding across the double bond.

- X bonds with one carbon while Y bonds with the other.

Molecule	X	Y
Br_2	Br	Br
H_2	H	H
H_2O	H	OH
HBr (or HCl)	H	Br (or Cl)

General example

✓*Quick check 1, 2, 4*

A summary of the reactions of propene

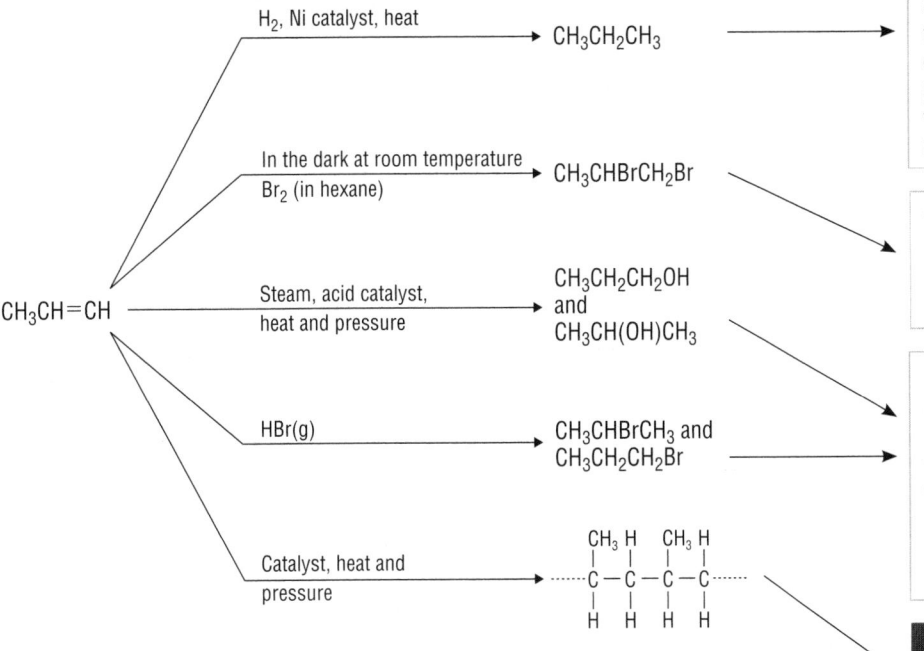

The reaction with hydrogen is used in the food industry to convert polyunsaturated vegetable oils to margarine.

This is the best test for alkenes. The bromine changes from orange to colourless.

NOTE: For unsymmetrical alkenes like propene, there are two isomeric products when X and Y are different, as in the addition of HOH (H_2O) and HBr.

Module 1

Examiner tip

When drawing polymers you are often asked to draw at least 4 carbons with dashed lines at each end to show that the chains carry on.

✔ *Quick check 4*

QUICK CHECK QUESTIONS

1 Give the conditions, names and structural formulae of the products of the reactions of
   a ethene;
   b *E*-but-2-ene with:
      i hydrogen;
      ii hydrogen bromide;
      iii bromine.
2 A hydrocarbon, X, consisted of 85.71% carbon and 14.29% hydrogen. Its molar mass was shown to be $42\,g\,mol^{-1}$.
   a Calculate its empirical formula.
   b Calculate its molecular formula and draw its displayed formula.
   c Draw the two products from the reaction of steam with X.
   d Draw the two products of the reaction of hydrogen bromide with X.
3 In the reaction mechanism for the addition of bromine to ethene, one of the bromine atoms is electron-deficient and acts as an *electrophile*. Explain the word in italics.
4 Animal fats are mainly saturated fats. Explain why, unlike vegetable oils used in the production of margarine, they cannot be hydrogenated.

UNIT 2

Addition polymerisation

Key words

- polymer
- monomer
- polymerisation
- saturated
- unsaturated

✓ *Quick check 1*

Polymers are large molecules consisting of repeating units of **monomers**. In this section you will revise how they are formed, their uses, and problems associated with their non-biodegradability.

Background

- **Addition polymers** are formed from alkenes, which are monomers.
- Many monomer units are derivatives of ethene. For example, chloroethene ($H_2C=CHCl$, or vinyl chloride); phenylethene ($C_6H_5CH=CH_2$, otherwise known as styrene).
- Polymerisation frequently uses high pressure, heat and a **catalyst**, called a Ziegler–Natta catalyst.

What happens during polymerisation?

- The double bonds in the alkenes open out to link all the monomers together with single bonds.
- The electrons in the π-bonds form the new σ-bonds between the monomer units.
- How this happens for ethene is shown in the diagram below.

Separate molecules — Unsaturated monomers

One large molecule — Saturated polymer

The easiest way to work out the structure is to think of the monomer as the repeat unit shown below. When you draw the structure of the addition polymer, either draw at least *four* carbons as shown below, or indicate a repeating structure as –[monomer unit]$_n$–.

W,X,Y and Z are atoms or groups e.g. CH_3

Draw polymer structure like this   or like this

Monomer   Polymer   Polymer

Examples

Monomer formula	Monomer name	Polymer formula	Polymer name
$CH_3CH=CH_2$	Propene	$-CH(CH_3)-CH_2-CH(CH_3)-CH_2-$ or $-[CH(CH_3)CH_2]_n-$	Poly(propene)
$CHCl=CH_2$	Chloroethene (vinyl chloride)	$-CHCl-CH_2-CHCl-CH_2-$ $-[CHClCH_2]_n-$	Poly(chloroethene) (PVC)
$CF_2=CF_2$	Tetrafluoroethene	$-CF_2-CF_2-CF_2-CF_2-$ $-[CF_2-CF_2]_n-$	Poly(tetrafluoroethene) (PTFE)

Problems with polymers

- Polymers such as polyethene contain either non-polar bonds (e.g. C–H) or strong bonds (e.g. C–F), making them unreactive. Because of this, they are non-biodegradable. Therefore they persist in the environment and cause a litter problem.

- Chemists are now developing many polymers, either from biological resources or from petrochemicals, that will biodegrade.

- The best way to deal with polymers is to recycle them, but this can be difficult because the different types are difficult to separate. Plastics made from recycled polymers are of a lower quality.

- If we try to dispose of them by burning, they give off toxic products such as carbon monoxide, oxides of nitrogen or hydrochloric acid, depending on the polymer's structure. It is particularly hazardous to burn poly(chloroethene) (polyvinylchloride, PVC), because toxic compounds such as HCl and polychlorinated biphenyls (PCBs) are formed. Chemists are devising ways of removing toxic compounds: for example, HCl is removed as hydrochloric acid by passing the waste gases up spray towers.

✓*Quick check 2 and 3*

- New processes are being developed by which polymers can be **cracked** to give new alkenes. Also, waste plastics are being used as fuels, for example in power generators.

- New polymers are being produced that are biodegradable and compostable. For example, polymers formed from isoprene are used to make babies' nappies and photographic film.

QUICK CHECK QUESTIONS

1 **a** Draw the displayed formulae of the following monomers:
     i ethene; **ii** propene; **iii** chloroethene; **iv** tetrafluoroethene.
   b For each monomer draw the resulting polymer, showing at least four carbons.

2 For each of the following polymers, give the possible polluting products of combustion:
   a poly(ethene)
   b poly(chloroethene).

3 **a** Draw the monomer unit that would lead to formation of the polymer shown below.

$$
\begin{array}{c}
\quad\;\; \text{CN}\;\;\; \text{CH}_3\;\; \text{CN}\;\;\; \text{CH}_3 \\
\quad\;\; | \quad\; | \quad\;\; | \quad\;\; | \\
---\text{C}-\text{C}-\text{C}-\text{C}--- \\
\quad\;\; | \quad\; | \quad\;\; | \quad\;\; | \\
\quad\;\; \text{H}\;\;\; \text{H}\;\;\; \text{H}\;\;\; \text{H}
\end{array}
$$

   b What pollutants might be formed by the combustion of this polymer?

UNIT 2

The alcohols

Key words

- alcohol
- homologous
- hydrogen bonds
- elimination
- combustion

Module 2

Here the chemistry of this important **homologous series** of compounds containing the OH group will be considered. You have already seen how they are named (page 47), and you will need to understand about hydrogen bonding, isomerism and fuels.

Background

- The alcohols are a homologous series containing the hydroxyl (–OH) group. Their general formula is $C_nH_{2n+1}OH$.
- The most important alcohols are methanol (CH_3OH) and ethanol (C_2H_5OH).
- Ethanol is produced on an industrial scale by the reaction of ethene with steam or by fermentation of sugars; methanol can be produced from wood.
- Alcohols are very soluble in water because they form **hydrogen bonds** with water.
- Alcohols are good fuels that burn cleanly and quickly to give CO_2 and H_2O.
- The main chemical reactions of alcohols concern the –OH group.

Physical properties of alcohols

✓ *Quick check 1*

- The alcohol molecule is polar, which leads to hydrogen bonding between the molecules.
- Alcohols have lower than expected **volatility** (higher than expected boiling points) because of the hydrogen bonding between the molecules.
- Short-chain alcohols are very soluble in water. This is because they can form hydrogen bonds with the water molecules (see figure on left).
- Alcohols can be recognised from their infrared spectra by absorption by the O–H bond (see page 68).

✓ *Quick check 2*

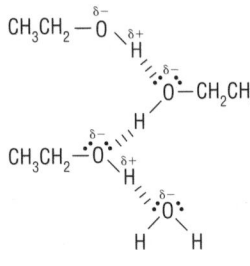

Properties common to all alcohols

Combustion

Alcohols burn in the presence of a plentiful supply of air (oxygen) to form carbon dioxide and water.

✓ *Quick check 3*

The reaction is **exothermic**, and because of their availability, ease of use and storage, alcohols make good fuels.

For example, methanol and ethanol are both used as fuels because they are both renewable and burn cleanly.

$$CH_3OH(l) + 1\tfrac{1}{2}O_2(g) \rightarrow CO_2(g) + 2H_2O(l) \text{ methanol from wood}$$

$$CH_3CH_2OH(l) + 3O_2 \rightarrow 2CO_2(g) + 3H_2O(l) \text{ ethanol from sugar cane}$$

Countries such as Brazil use ethanol mixed with petrol or 93% ethanol as fuels. The source of the ethanol is the sugar in sugar cane, making ethanol a renewable fuel.

Elimination of water

When alcohols are heated in the presence of an acid **catalyst** (concentrated phosphoric or sulfuric acid), water is eliminated from alcohols to give alkenes.

✔ *Quick check 4*

Examples:

$$CH_3CH_2OH \xrightarrow{\text{acid catalyst and heat}} C_2H_4 + H_2O$$

$$CH_3CH(OH)CH_3 \xrightarrow{\text{acid catalyst and heat}} CH_3CH=CH_2 + H_2O$$

Esterification

In the presence of an acid catalyst, alcohols react with carboxylic acids to form sweet-smelling liquids called esters.

Hint

Carboxylic acids contain the –COOH (carboxyl) group. Ethanoic acid (CH_3COOH) is an example.

Example:

$$CH_3CH_2OH + CH_3COOH \xrightarrow{\text{acid catalyst and heat}} CH_3COOCH_2CH_3 + H_2O$$

| alcohol (e.g. ethanol) | carboxylic acid (e.g. ethanoic acid) | | ester (ethyl ethanoate) | water |

✔ *Quick check 5*

Summary of the reactions common to all alcohols

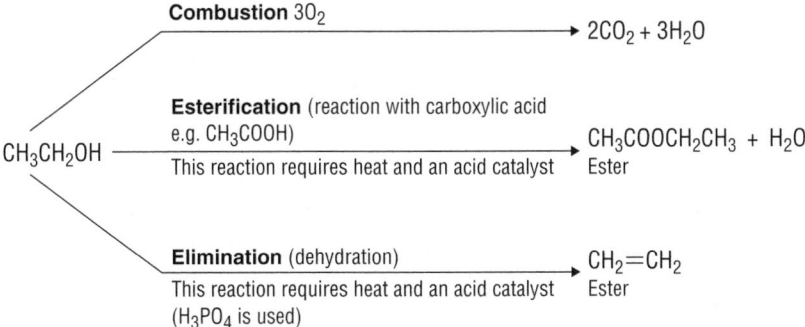

CH_3CH_2OH

Combustion $3O_2$ $\longrightarrow$ $2CO_2 + 3H_2O$

Esterification (reaction with carboxylic acid e.g. CH_3COOH)
This reaction requires heat and an acid catalyst $\longrightarrow$ $CH_3COOCH_2CH_3 + H_2O$ Ester

Elimination (dehydration)
This reaction requires heat and an acid catalyst (H_3PO_4 is used) $\longrightarrow$ $CH_2=CH_2$ Ester

QUICK CHECK QUESTIONS

1. **a** Give the names and structural formulae of all the alcohols with the following molecular formulae: **i** C_3H_8O; **ii** $C_4H_{10}O$
   b Name the alcohol with the structural formula $CH_3CH(CH_3)CH_2CH_2OH$.

2. **a** **i** Draw a diagram of a molecule of ethanol showing the dipoles present.
   ii Explain why these dipoles are present.
   b Using diagrams, explain why ethanol is very soluble in water.

3. Propan-1-ol burns in a plentiful supply of oxygen.
   a Give the equation for the reaction.
   b Both ethanol and methanol are considered renewable fuels. Explain why.

4. Give the names and structural formulae of the organic products of the following reactions:

   a $CH_3CH_2CH_2OH \xrightarrow{\text{acid catalyst and heat}}$

   b $CH_3CH_2CHOHCH_3 \xrightarrow{\text{acid catalyst and heat}}$ two products

5. Complete the following equations:

   a $CH_3CH_2OH + CH_3COOH \xrightarrow{\text{acid catalyst}}$

   b $CH_3CH_2CH_2OH + HCOOH \xrightarrow{\text{acid catalyst}}$

   c $CH_3OH + CH_3COOH \xrightarrow{\text{acid catalyst}}$

Types of alcohol

Key words

- primary
- secondary
- tertiary
- fermentation

✓ *Quick check 1*

Classification of alcohols

- Primary (1°) – on the carbon with the OH group there are two hydrogen atoms.
- Secondary (2°) – on the carbon with the OH group there is only one hydrogen.
- Tertiary (3°) – on the carbon with the OH group there are no hydrogens.

Examples

Primary	Secondary	Tertiary
Butan-1-ol	Butan-2-ol	2-methylpropan-2-ol
$CH_3CH_2CH_2\textbf{CH}_2OH$	$CH_3CH_2\textbf{CH}(OH)CH_3$	$(CH_3)_3\textbf{C}OH$

Hint

Ethanol in the form of wine can be oxidised slowly to ethanoic acid (vinegar) in the presence of oxygen.

✓ *Quick check 2*

How do we distinguish between the three types?

- The types of alcohol can be distinguished by their ability to be oxidised by an acidified solution of potassium dichromate(VI). If a reaction occurs, the acidified potassium dichromate(VI) changes colour from orange to blue-green.
- The primary and secondary alcohols each have at least one hydrogen atom on the carbon with the hydroxyl (OH) group. One of these hydrogens can be removed along with the hydrogen on the OH group; in other words, these two types can be oxidised.

Example 1

A primary alcohol, butan-1-ol. If we heat it with the oxidising agent and distil the product immediately, an aldehyde is the organic product (e.g. butanal, below).

$$CH_3CH_2CH_2CH_2OH(l) + [O] \rightarrow CH_3CH_2CH_2CHO(l) + H_2O(l)$$

Examiner tip

Note that the [O] comes from the oxidising agent, acidified potassium dichromate.

If we use excess acidified potassium dichromate(VI) and then heat the mixture under reflux, further oxidation can occur to give a carboxylic acid, butanoic acid.

$$CH_3CH_2CH_2CH_2OH(l) + 2[O] \rightarrow CH_3CH_2CH_2COOH(l) + H_2O(l)$$

Example 2

A secondary alcohol, butan-2-ol. In this reaction a ketone is the organic product.

$$CH_3CH_2CH(OH)CH_3(l) + [O] \rightarrow CH_3CH_2COCH_3(l) + H_2O(l)$$

The secondary alcohol cannot be oxidised further by the acidified dichromate, even if the dichromate is in excess.

The tertiary alcohols have no hydrogen atoms on the carbon with the OH group; therefore they cannot be oxidised and there is no reaction. The acidified potassium dichromate(VI) remains orange.

Industrial production of ethanol

Because ethanol has several important uses, it is necessary to prepare it on a large scale. There are two main methods, and they are very different.

Method 1 – fermentation of sugars using yeast

- Juices of fruits, which contain sugars, are fermented in the presence of yeast.
- The yeast contains enzymes that catalyse the reactions.
- The overall equation is:

$$C_6H_{12}O_6(aq) \rightarrow 2C_2H_5OH(aq) + 2CO_2(g)$$

- When the ethanol concentration reaches 15%, the yeast dies and the reaction stops.
- The liquid produced in this way has a taste dependent on the source of the fruit from which it was made. If it is further concentrated by fractional distillation, spirits can be obtained.

Method 2 – hydration of ethene

- In this method, ethene and steam are passed at 300 °C and high pressure over a catalyst of phosphoric acid on silica pellets.

$$C_2H_4(g) + H_2O(g) \rightarrow C_2H_5OH(g)$$

- This is industrial alcohol and is not used as a drink.

Hint

Countries such as Brazil, with few oil reserves, obtain alcohol from sugar. It is made more concentrated and then used as a fuel for cars. Because the source of the ethanol is sugar, which can be grown again and again, ethanol is a renewable fuel.

✓*Quick check 4*

Module 2

Main uses of alcohols

Alcohol	Uses
Methanol	In the manufacture of phenol–formaldehyde resins (Bakelite) and Perspex (poly(methyl methacrylate))
	In fuels as an additive to improve combustion, or as a fuel
Ethanol	As a fuel for cars in several countries
	As a solvent for several organic chemicals
	As a beverage (in wines, beers and sprits)
	In the preparation of esters

QUICK CHECK QUESTIONS

1   Classify the following alcohols as primary, secondary or tertiary:
    a $CH_3CH_2CH_2OH$
    b $CH_3CH_2CH(OH)CH_2CH_3$
    c $C_6H_5CH_2OH$
    d $(CH_3)_3COH$
    e $C_6H_5CH(OH)CH_3$.

2   Explain why, when wine is left open for any length of time, it starts to taste of vinegar (vinegar is ethanoic acid – a carboxylic acid).

3   Explain how you can distinguish between 2-methylpropan-2-ol and butan-2-ol. State any observations that may be made.

4   Explain why production of alcohol by fermentation can never produce 100% alcohol straight away.

UNIT 2

The halogenoalkanes

Key words
- halide
- reactivity

✓*Quick check 1*

The halogenoalkanes are an important homologous series because they are so useful as intermediates in the synthesis of other organic compounds, especially when a longer carbon chain is needed. They also have important large-scale uses.

Background facts

- All halogenoalkanes contain at least one halogen (abbreviated to 'X') attached to a carbon atom (C–X).
- If they contain just one halogen atom and there are no multiple bonds, their general formula is $C_nH_{2n+1}X$.
- The C–X bond is polarised, leaving the carbon atom electron-deficient and open to attack by nucleophiles [e.g. water and OH⁻ ions from KOH(aq)].
- Because the halide ion (X⁻) is stable, it is a good leaving group and therefore is substituted reasonably easily by the nucleophile.
- The reaction mechanism undergone by the halogenoalkanes when they are substituted is nucleophilic substitution. This literally means substitution by a nucleophile.
- The best test for halogenoalkanes is to warm with water in ethanol and then test for the halide ion using aqueous silver nitrate solution (see page 37).
- There are three types of halogenoalkane – primary, secondary and tertiary.

The strength of the C–X bond is in the following order (strongest first):

C–F > C–Cl > C–Br > C–I

The reactivity of the halogenoalkanes is in the reverse order:

most reactive → least reactive

C–I > C–Br > C–Cl > C–F

The reactivity of the halogenoalkanes depends on the breaking of the C–X bond. As the C–F bond is the strongest, it is the hardest to break, and therefore fluoroalkanes are the least reactive of the halogenoalkanes.

- Halogenoalkanes, especially those containing chlorine and fluorine, have several uses related to their properties.
- Chlorofluorocarbons (CFCs), which were once used as refrigerants and in fire extinguishers, are very stable and persist in the environment. They catalyse the decomposition of ozone, leading to depletion of the ozone layer.
- Unsaturated halogenoalkanes, such as chloroethene ($CHCl=CH_2$) and tetrafluoroethene ($CF_2=CF_2$), act just like normal alkenes and can be used to make polymers. For example, chloroethene is used to make poly(chloroethene).

Remember

A nucleophile is a molecule or ion that can donate a pair of electrons. A nucleophile is quite often represented as Nu⁻ or Nu:⁻.

✓*Quick check 3*

Types of halogenoalkane

1. **Primary (1°)**. On the carbon with the halogen, there are two hydrogen atoms.
2. **Secondary (2°)**. On the carbon with the halogen, there is only one hydrogen.
3. **Tertiary (3°)**. On the carbon with the halogen, there are no hydrogens.

✓*Quick check 2*

Examples of halogenoalkanes

Primary	Secondary	Tertiary
1-iodobutane	2-chlorobutane	2-bromo-2-methylpropane
$CH_3CH_2CH_2CH_2I$	$CH_3CH_2CHClCH_3$	$(CH_3)_3CBr$

Reactions of halogenoalkanes

- The electron-deficient carbon in the carbon–halogen bond is liable to attack from nucleophiles with their lone-pair electrons.
- The carbon cannot form more than four bonds, so the nucleophile (Nu:⁻) forms a covalent bond with the carbon and the halogen leaves as a X:⁻ (e.g. Br:⁻) ion.

The general mechanism for reaction of a halogenoalkane and a nucleophile (Nu:⁻) is shown below:

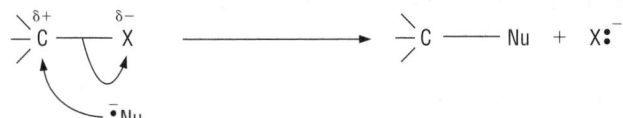

The nucleophile approaches the electron-deficient carbon and, using its lone-pair electrons, forms a dative covalent bond with the carbon.

The halide ion (X:⁻) is stable and is able to leave the halogenoalkane. The nucleophile has replaced (substituted) it.

QUICK CHECK QUESTIONS

1. Analysis of a halogenoalkane, **A**, showed that it contained 29.3% carbon, 5.7% hydrogen and 65.0% bromine by mass (relative atomic masses Br = 79.9; C = 12.0; H = 1.0).
   a. Calculate the empirical formula of **A**.
   b. Its relative molecular mass is 122.9. Calculate its molecular formula.
   c. Draw the displayed formulae for the structural isomers of **A**.
2. Give the structural formulae and names of the four structural isomers of bromobutane (C_4H_9Br).
3. a. When halogenoalkanes are used for synthesis of carbon compounds, fluoroalkanes are never used. Explain why.
   b. Suggest a reason why bromoalkanes are used in syntheses in preference to iodoalkanes.

Module 2

Reactions of the halogenoalkanes

The reactions you need to learn are those with water and aqueous alkalis such as sodium hydroxide.

Halogenoalkanes, especially those with C–I and C–Br bonds, are useful intermediates in synthetic pathways, as other groups can be introduced into the molecule easily. Bromoalkanes are probably the most useful (see page 64).
Example:

$$CH_3CH_2Br + NaOH \xrightarrow{\text{heat}} CH_3CH_2OH + NaBr$$

Halogenoalkanes also react with water in a similar way.
Example:

$$CH_3CH_2Br + H_2O \xrightarrow{\text{heat}} CH_3CH_2OH + HBr$$

Comparing reactivities of the halogenoalkanes

✔ *Quick check 1 and 2*

Hint

The reaction involving water can be called hydrolysis – the water (*hydro-*) molecule is split up (*-lysis*).

An experiment to compare their reactivities:

1 In three separate test tubes, warm equal volumes of $AgNO_3$ solution in ethanol to 50 °C.

2 Add a few drops of three comparable halogenoalkanes (e.g. 1-chlorobutane, 1-bromobutane and 1-iodobutane) to each tube. The first reaction is:

$$\text{R-X(l)} + H_2O(l) \rightarrow \text{ROH(l)} + H^+(aq) + X^-(aq)$$

3 Silver ions (from $AgNO_3$) then react with the halide (X^-) ions to give a precipitate of silver halide:

✔ *Quick check 3*

$$Ag^+(aq) + X^-(aq) \rightarrow AgX(s)$$

This precipitate will make the mixture go cloudy.

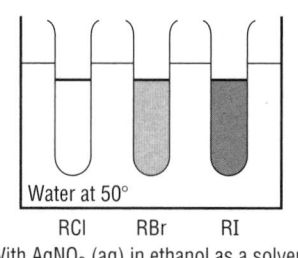

Water at 50°

RCl   RBr   RI

With $AgNO_3$ (aq) in ethanol as a solvent
(R is an alkyl group)

5 The speed with which the mixture goes cloudy is an indication of the speed of the reaction and hence the reactivity of the C–halogen bond.

6 It is found that the iodoalkane reacts most quickly. Therefore it is the bond enthalpy of the C–halogen bond that determines the rate of hydrolysis of the halogenoalkane.

Uses of halogenoalkanes

The C–F and C–Cl bonds are strong, so compounds containing these are relatively unreactive and stable under normal atmospheric conditions. In the presence of a nucleophile, they are reactive (see page 65).

Compounds containing both chlorine and fluorine are called chlorofluorocarbons (CFCs). Since it was discovered that CFCs lead to depletion of the ozone layer, their use has been discontinued and chemists have had to find alternatives. These less-damaging alternatives are hydrofluorocarbons (HFCs). In these compounds, the C–F bond is so strong it does not break, even in the ozone layer, unlike the C–Cl bond in CFCs. Unfortunately, HFCs have a high greenhouse factor (see page 78) and contribute to global warming.

✔*Quick check 4*

Module 2

The uses of HFCs are given in the table below.

Use	Properties and reason(s) for use
Refrigerants and air-conditioning plant	Highly effective, energy-efficient refrigerants that vaporise easily
Medical aerosols	Volatile, so easily vaporised along with other contents of aerosol can
Fire extinguishers	Unreactive, so do not burn easily Denser than air, so sink and smother fire
Dry-cleaning	Good solvents for grease and fats

QUICK CHECK QUESTIONS

1 Explain why the reaction between 2-bromobutane and sodium hydroxide is described as a nucleophilic substitution reaction.
2 Give a full balanced equation for the reactions between 1,2-dibromoethane and aqueous KOH.
3 Explain how you could show that the C–Br bond is more easily broken than the C–Cl bond.
4 Explain why hydrofluorocarbons have the following uses:
   a refrigerants
   b fire extinguishers
   c dry-cleaning.

UNIT 2

Infrared spectroscopy

Infrared spectroscopy is a very useful technique in determining a compound's structure. It relies on the fact that different bonds in compounds absorb at different frequencies in the infrared region of the spectrum. In infrared analysis, the wavenumber (the reciprocal of wavelength) is used instead of frequency or wavelength, and is measured in cm^{-1}. The functional groups and bonds you will be asked about are given in the table below, along with their wavenumbers. Note that you do not have to remember these in the exam, as they will be given in your data book.

Functional group/bond	Wavenumber/cm^{-1}
Hydroxyl (–OH) hydrogen bonded in carboxylic acids	Broad, 2500–3300
O–H 'hydrogen bonded' in alcohols	Less broad, 3200–3550
C–H in organic compounds	2850–3100
Carbonyl group (C=O) in aldehydes, ketones and carboxylic acids	1640–1750
C–O in alcohols, esters and carboxylic acids	1000–1300

Some typical spectra for compounds with these infrared absorptions are shown on the next page.

Note the following:

- The alcohol shows a strong broad absorption between 3200 and 3550 cm^{-1} due to the O–H hydrogen bonding, and no absorption at approximately 1700 cm^{-1} because there is no carbonyl group (C=O) (spectrum I).

- The carboxylic acid shows a very broad absorption at around 2500–3000 cm^{-1} because of the O–H, and at approximately 1700 cm^{-1} due to the group (spectrum II).

- The aldehyde and ketone show absorption at around 1700 cm^{-1}, but no strong broad absorption at 3200–3550 (spectra III, IV).

- For the alcohols, esters and carboxylic acids, there is a C–O absorption at 1000–1300 cm^{-1}, but this is harder to see.

QUICK CHECK QUESTIONS

1. A compound, X, gives a strong, broad absorption at around 3300–3400 cm^{-1} but none at 1700 cm^{-1}.
   a. Which functional group is present in X?
   b. To which homologous series does it belong?
2. Describe what changes you would see in the infrared spectra when ethanol (CH_3CH_2OH) is oxidised to ethanal (CH_3CHO) and then to ethanoic acid (CH_3COOH).
3. Ethanol is isomeric with a substance called ethoxyethane (CH_3OCH_3). Explain how the two compounds can be distinguished using infrared spectroscopy.
4. Explain how you can distinguish between propan-2-ol ($CH_3CH(OH)CH_3$) and propanoic acid (CH_3CH_2COOH).

I Alcohol

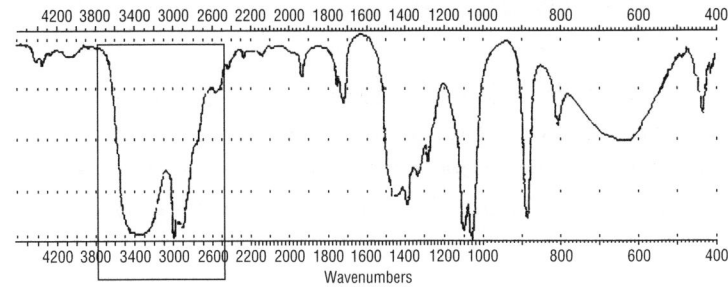

II Carboxylic acid

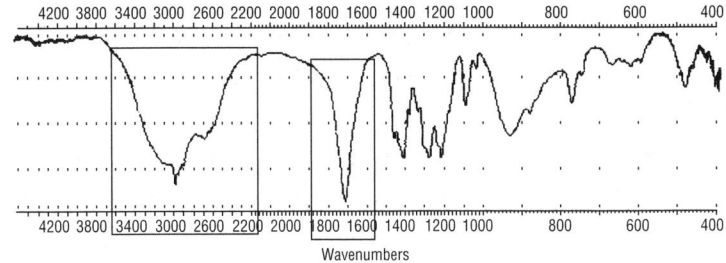

III Carbonyl-aldehyde

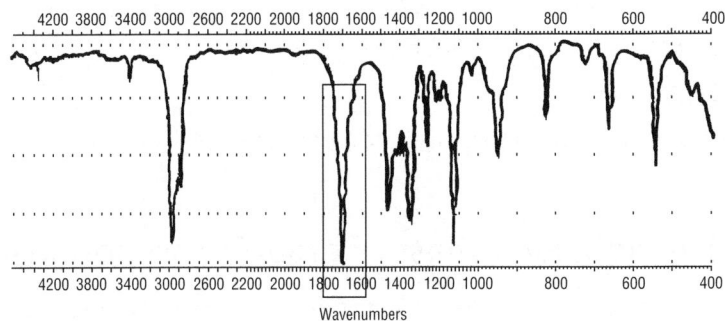

IV Carbonyl-ketone

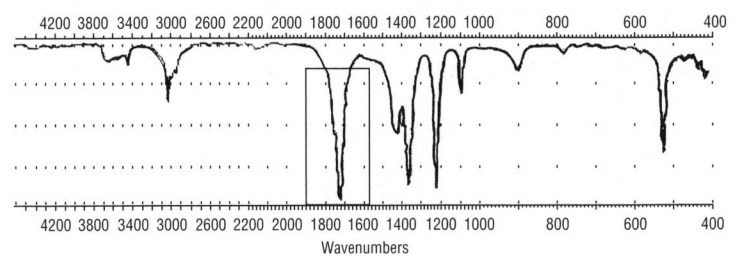

Mass spectrometry

Key words

- ions
- radicals
- mass/charge ratio
- fragmentation

The mass spectrometer is used to find the relative abundance of isotopes of the elements in our atmosphere. It has also been used to find the isotopic composition of the elements on Mars, and to estimate the amounts of toxins in our food. You do not have to know how the mass spectrometer works, but you will need to know its uses, especially in organic chemistry.

Using mass spectrometry in analysing organic compounds

- When elements and compounds are passed through a mass spectrometer, positive ions are produced, which can be separated and analysed according to their mass/charge (or m/z) ratio.

- The mass spectrum of an organic compound is a plot of the relative intensity of the signal produced by the ion (which is a measure of its abundance charge ratio against its mass/charge ratio).

- When organic compounds are passed through a mass spectrometer, they break up (fragment) to give positive **ions** and **radicals**.

- The ions can be detected by the spectrometer. For example, ethanol (CH_3CH_2OH) will fragment in several ways. One way is between the –OH group and the CH_3CH_2– group to give the $CH_3CH_2^+$ ion. This ion shows up at $m/z = 29$.

  $$CH_3CH_2OH^+ \rightarrow CH_3CH_2^+ + \cdot OH$$

- The fragmentation pattern can be used to identify compounds or to distinguish between them.

Finding the relative molecular mass of organic compounds

- One very important peak on the mass spectrum of an organic compound is the peak that corresponds to the molecular ion – the molecular ion peak.

- The m/z ratio for this peak is the relative molecular mass of the compound.

- This peak is the last large peak on the mass spectrum.

The mass spectrum for ethanol (CH_3CH_2OH) is shown here.

The molecular ion peak is the peak at 46, and this corresponds to the relative molecular mass ($2 \times 12.0 + 6 \times 1.00 + 1 \times 16.0$).

Hint

If you are asked to give the equation for fragmentation, don't forget the radical.

✔ *Quick check 1*

✔ *Quick check 2*

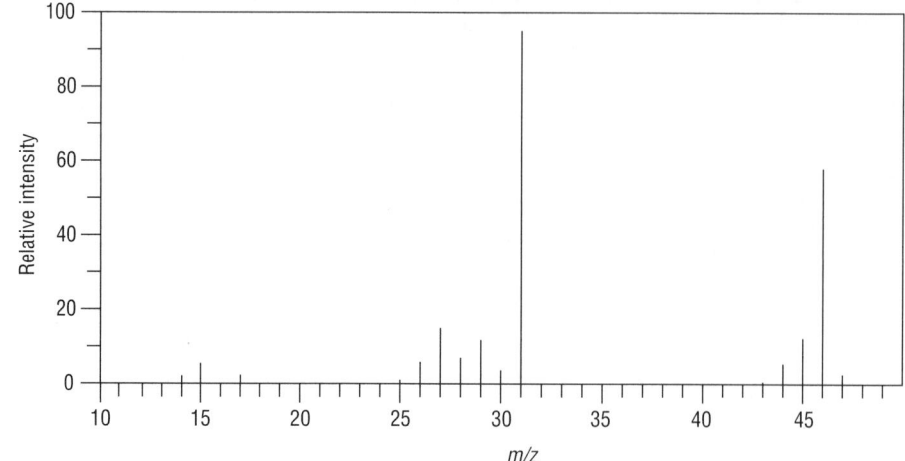

Using fragmentation patterns to identify organic compounds

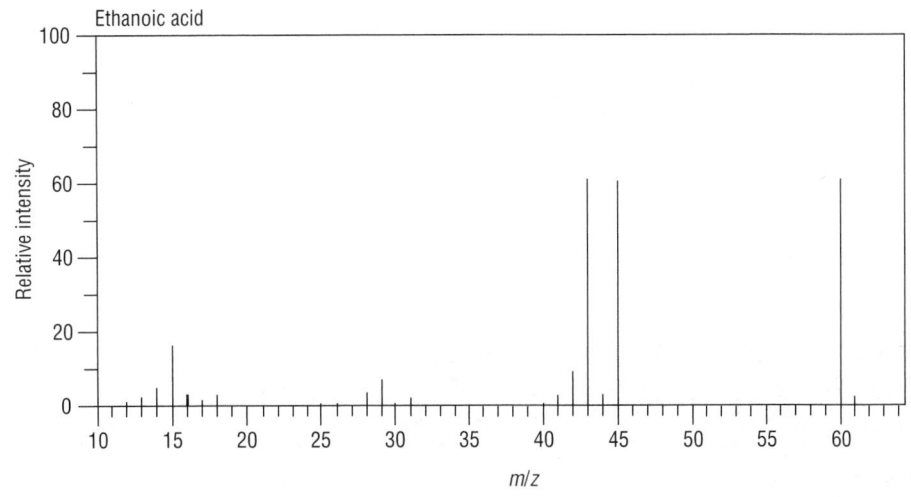

For example, the two compounds ethanoic acid (CH_3COOH) and methyl methanoate ($HCOOCH_3$) are isomers. Their mass spectra are given below.

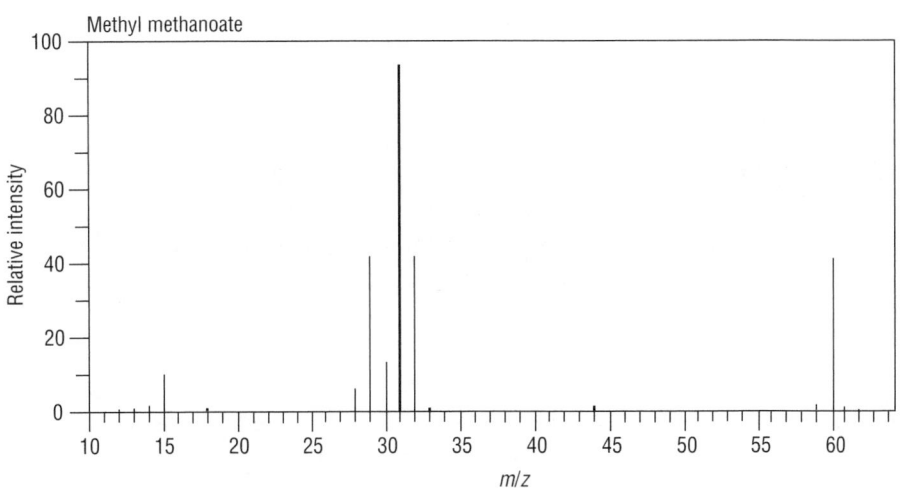

What are the similarities between the two spectra?

1 They both have peaks at $m/z = 60$
   Explanation: This is the last large peak on the spectrum. It is the molecular ion peak, and gives the relative molecular mass of the compound. This agrees with the value calculated by adding up the relative atomic masses ($2 \times 12.0 + 4 \times 1.00 + 2 \times 16.0$).

2 They both have a peak at $m/z = 15$.
   Explanation: This is caused by the CH_3^+ ion, by the fragmentations:

   $CH_3COOH^+ \rightarrow CH_3^+ + \cdot COOH$
   $HCOOCH_3^+ \rightarrow HCOO\cdot + CH_3^+$

What are the differences between the two spectra?

1 The spectrum for CH_3COOH has a peak at $m/z = 45$. This is not present for methyl methanoate.
   Explanation: This is caused by the $COOH^+$ ion. This is not possible for methyl methanoate. The fragmentation that causes this is:

   $CH_3COOH^+ \rightarrow COOH^+ + CH_3\cdot$

2 The spectrum for CH_3COOH has a peak at $m/z = 43$. This is not present for methyl methanoate.
   Explanation: This is caused by the CH_3CO^+ ion. This is not possible for methyl methanoate. The fragmentation that causes this is:

   $CH_3COOH^+ \rightarrow CH_3CO^+ + \cdot OH$

QUICK CHECK QUESTIONS

1 At what m/z value would you find the molecular ion peak for butan-2-one ($CH_3COCH_2CH_3$)?
2 Explain why the mass spectrum of ethanol (CH_3CH_2OH) shows peaks at m/z values of 15, 29 and 31.

Module 2

UNIT 2

Enthalpy changes

Module 3

Key words

- enthalpy
- profile
- exothermic
- endothermic
- activation energy

Hint

The units of ΔH are $kJ\,mol^{-1}$.

Hint

Δ is the Greek character delta. It is the symbol for the difference between two values.

Enthalpy, H, is the heat content stored in a chemical system. When a chemical reaction takes place and there is an exchange of energy with the surroundings, ΔH, then:

$$\Delta H = H_{products} - H_{reactants}$$

Chemical reactions can be divided into two types – those that cause a rise in temperature and those that cause a fall in temperature. The properties and descriptions of these changes are shown in the table below.

Type of thermochemical change	Properties		Examples
	Temperature of surroundings	Enthalpy of chemical system	
Exothermic	Increases	Decreases. ΔH is negative because the system has lost energy to the surroundings	*Combustion* of hydrocarbon fuels Oxidation of carbohydrates in *respiration*
Endothermic	Decreases	Increases. ΔH is positive because the system has gained energy from the surroundings	The formation of glucose in *photosynthesis* The *decomposition* of metal carbonates, e.g. $CaCO_3$

Enthalpy profile diagrams

- A chemical reaction can be regarded as breaking bonds followed by making bonds. Breaking bonds needs energy, so energy must be put into the reaction.

✔ *Quick check 1*

- The minimum energy needed to start a reaction is called the activation energy.

- After that, bonds are made, which releases energy. Enthalpy profile diagrams compare the enthalpies of the reactants with those of the products.

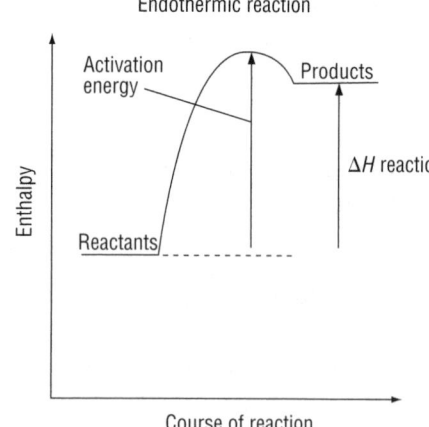

✔ *Quick check 2*

- When bonds are broken, energy is taken in: ΔH is positive.

- When bonds are made, energy is released: ΔH is negative.

- It follows that if the bonds *made* are stronger than the bonds *broken*, then there is an overall *decrease* in enthalpy and the reaction is **exothermic**.

- If the bonds *broken* are stronger than the bonds *made*, then there is an overall *increase* in enthalpy and the reaction is **endothermic**.

Types of enthalpy change

The table below summarises the different types of enthalpy changes are measured under standard conditions, at:

- pressure = 100 kPa
- temperature = 298 K
- concentration of solutions = 1 mol dm^{-3}.

Hint

The superscript $^{\ominus}$ denotes standard conditions.

✓ *Quick check 3*

Enthalpy change	Symbol	Definition	Examples and equations
Standard enthalpy change of formation	$\Delta H_f^{\ominus}$	Enthalpy change when 1 mole of a compound is formed from its constituent elements in their standard states, under standard conditions **$\Delta H_f^{\ominus}$ of an element in its standard state = 0**	Water, $\Delta H_f^{\ominus} = -286\,kJ\,mol^{-1}$ $H_2(g) + \frac{1}{2}O_2(g) \rightarrow H_2O(l)$ Ethanol (C_2H_5OH), $\Delta H_f^{\ominus} = -277\,kJ\,mol^{-1}$ $2C(s) + 3H_2(g) + \frac{1}{2}O_2(g) \rightarrow C_2H_5OH(l)$ Hydrazine (N_2H_4), $\Delta H_f^{\ominus} = +50.6\,kJ\,mol^{-1}$ $N_2(g) + 2H_2(g) \rightarrow N_2H_4(l)$
Standard enthalpy change of combustion	$\Delta H_c^{\ominus}$	Enthalpy change when 1 mole of a substance (element or compound) reacts completely with oxygen under standard conditions	All these reactions are *exothermic*, so $\Delta H_c^{\ominus}$ is always *negative* Hydrogen, $\Delta H_c^{\ominus} = -286\,kJ\,mol^{-1}$ $H_2(g) + \frac{1}{2}O_2(g) \rightarrow H_2O(l)$ Ethanol, $\Delta H_c^{\ominus} = -1367\,kJ\,mol^{-1}$ $C_2H_5OH(l) + 3O_2(g) \rightarrow 2CO_2(g) + 3H_2O(l)$
Standard enthalpy change of reaction	$\Delta H_r^{\ominus}$	The enthalpy change that accompanies a reaction under standard conditions in the molar quantities expressed in a chemical equation, all reactants and products being in their standard states	Decomposition of calcium carbonate – an *endothermic* reaction $\Delta H_r^{\ominus} = +178\,kJ\,mol^{-1}$ $CaCO_3(s) \rightarrow CaO(s) + CO_2(g)$ Reaction of nitrogen and ammonia – an *exothermic* reaction $\Delta H_r^{\ominus} = -92\,kJ\,mol^{-1}$ $N_2(g) + 3H_2(g) \rightarrow 2NH_3(g)$

Module 3

✓ *Quick check 4*

Average bond enthalpies (ΔH_d)

- Covalent bonds have different strengths. The average enthalpy change required to break 1 mole of a given type of bond by **homolytic fission** in the molecules of a gaseous species is called the **average bond enthalpy** (ΔH_d).

- For example, the average bond enthalpy of the H–Br bond is 366 kJ mol^{-1}. For this bond, there is only one possible value for ΔH_d.

✓ *Quick check 5*

- For bonds in polyatomic molecules, such as CH_4, the bond energies for the successive broken bonds differ. To overcome this problem, the bond enthalpy is calculated by taking their average, hence the term average bond enthalpy.

QUICK CHECK QUESTIONS

1 When iron is added to copper sulfate solution, the temperature rises.
   a What type of thermochemical reaction is this?
   b Is the sign for $\Delta H_r^{\ominus}$ plus or minus?
   c Explain your answer to (b).
2 The decomposition of $CaCO_3$ (to give CaO and CO_2) is an endothermic reaction. Draw an energy profile diagram to represent the enthalpy change in this reaction. On your diagram, label the activation energy and enthalpy change of reaction.

3 Define the terms a standard conditions; b standard enthalpy change of formation.
4 Give the equations that represent the standard enthalpy changes of formation and combustion of the following:
   a $C_2H_6(g)$; b $CO(g)$; c $CH_3OH(l)$; d $N_2H_4(l)$.
5 The energy required for breaking all the N–H bonds in $NH_3(g)$ is 1173 kJ mol^{-1}. What is the ΔH_d for the N–H bond?

UNIT 2

Calculating enthalpy changes

From average bond enthalpies (ΔH_d)

$\Delta H_{reaction}$ = ΔH_d of all the bonds in the reactants − ΔH_d of all the bonds in the products

$$
\begin{array}{l}
\text{H} \\
| \\
\text{H–C–H} \quad + \quad \text{Br–Br} \\
| \\
\text{H}
\end{array}
\qquad
\rightarrow
\begin{array}{l}
\text{H} \\
| \\
\text{H–C–Br} \\
| \\
\text{H}
\end{array}
\qquad + \quad \text{H–Br}
$$

$4 \times (413) + 1 \times (193)$ $-[3 \times (413) + 1 \times (290)] + -1 \times (366)$

1652   + 193 -1529 -366

$\Delta H_{reaction}$ = $(1652 + 193) - (1529 + 366)$

= $1845 - 1895 = -50\,kJ\,mol^{-1}$

How to calculate enthalpy changes experimentally

For solutions, use this equation to calculate the enthalpy change of a reaction:

energy change in surroundings = $m \times c \times \Delta T$

m is the mass, but in solution we can assume mass in g = volume in cm^3.

c is a constant, the specific heat capacity of water c is $4.2\,J\,g^{-1}\,K^{-1}$.

ΔT is the difference in temperature from the start of the reaction to the highest or lowest temperature reached.

■ WORKED EXAMPLE

$50\,cm^3$ of concentrated sulfuric acid, $20.0\,mol\,dm^{-3}$, was added to $950\,cm^3$ of water at a temperature of 19.0 °C. The solution was stirred gently until the maximum temperature was reached at 28.0 °C. What is the enthalpy change for this reaction?

STEP 1 Write down the equation you will use:

energy change in surroundings = $mc\Delta T$

STEP 2 Write down the values for the symbols m, c and ΔT:

$m = 950 + 50 = 1000\,cm^3$; $c = 4.2\,Jg^{-1}k^{-1}$; $\Delta T = 28 - 19 = 9\,°C$

STEP 3 Do the calculation: energy change = $1000 \times 4.2 \times 9 = 37\,800\,J = \textbf{37.8\,kJ}$

This is an *exothermic* reaction so it has a *negative* sign: **−37.8 kJ**

What is the enthalpy change per mole of sulfuric acid?

STEP 4 Calculate the amount, in moles, of sulfuric acid:

$$\text{amount (mol)} = \frac{\text{vol (cm}^3)}{1000} \times \text{concentration} = \frac{50.0}{1000} \times 20.0 = 1.00\,mol$$

STEP 5 Divide the ΔH value by the number of moles:

$$\frac{37.8}{1.00} = \textbf{−37.8\,kJ\,mol}^{-1}$$

Hess' law

Hess' law states that for any chemical change, the enthalpy change is the same whatever route is taken to make the change.

Applying Hess' law to the figure on the left:

$$\Delta H_1 = \Delta H_2 + \Delta H_3$$

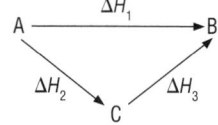

Calculating enthalpy changes indirectly using Hess's law

Many enthalpy changes are impossible to determine directly because the activation energies for these reactions are too high. For example, the reaction:

$$C(s) + 2H_2(g) \rightarrow CH_4(g)$$

does not occur because of its very high activation energy. To find the $\Delta H_f^{\ominus}$ for CH_4, we can make a Hess' cycle. For example, in the figure above, if the unknown enthalpy change was ΔH_1, and ΔH_2 and ΔH_3 could be determined experimentally, by applying Hess' law ΔH_1 can be found by substituting the values for the other two enthalpy changes.

Two ways of finding ΔH indirectly by Hess' law are summarised in the table below.

Data given	Hess' cycle	Summary equation
$\Delta H_c^{\ominus}$	Reactants $\xrightarrow{\Delta H_r}$ Products ΔH_c reactants $\searrow$ $\swarrow$ ΔH_c products Products of combustion	$\Delta H_r^{\ominus} = \Sigma\Delta H_c^{\ominus}$ (reactants) $- \Sigma\Delta H_c^{\ominus}$ (products) Σ is the symbol for 'sum of'
$\Delta H_f^{\ominus}$	Reactants $\xrightarrow{\Delta H_r}$ Products ΔH_f reactants $\nwarrow$ $\nearrow$ ΔH_f products Elements	$\Delta H_r^{\ominus} = \Sigma\Delta H_f^{\ominus}$ (products) $- \Sigma\Delta H_f^{\ominus}$ (reactants)

✔ *Quick check 2*

■ WORKED EXAMPLE 2

Calculate the $\Delta H_r^{\ominus}$ for the following reaction:

$$2NO_2(g) \rightarrow N_2O_4(g) \text{ given that: } \Delta H_f^{\ominus}(NO_2) = +33.2\,kJ\,mol^{-1}$$
$$\Delta H_f^{\ominus}(N_2O_4) = +9.2\,kJ\,mol^{-1}$$

STEP 1 Use the summary equation (or Hess's cycle) to calculate the heat of reaction.

$$\boldsymbol{\Delta H_r^{\ominus} = \Sigma\Delta H_f^{\ominus} \text{ (products)} - \Sigma\Delta H_f^{\ominus} \text{ (reactants)}}$$

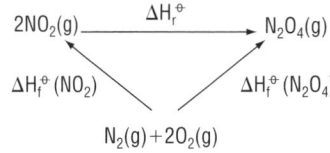

STEP 2 Put in the values for $\Delta H_f^{\ominus}$s:

$$\Delta H_r^{\ominus} = \Delta H_f^{\ominus}(N_2O_4) - 2\Delta H_f^{\ominus}(NO_2) = +9.2 - (2 \times 33.2) = -57.2\,kJ\,mol^{-1}$$

QUICK CHECK QUESTIONS

$\Delta H_d/kJ\,mol^{-1}$	$\Delta H_c/kJ\,mol^{-1}$	$\Delta H_f^{\ominus}/kJ\,mol^{-1}$
C–H 413; C=O 805; O–H 464; O=O 498 C=C 612; Cl–Cl 243; H–Cl 432; C–Cl 436	C(s) –394; H_2(g) –286;	NO(g) +90.2 N_2O(g) +82 NO_2(g) +33.2; N_2H_4 +50.6; H_2O(l) –286

1 Using ΔH_d find the $\Delta H_r^{\ominus}$ for the following reactions:
   a $C_2H_4 + 3O_2 \rightarrow 2CO_2 + 2H_2O$;
   b $CH_4 + Cl_2 \rightarrow CH_3Cl + HCl$

2 Find the standard enthalpy change of reaction for the following reactions:
   a $N_2H_4(l) + O_2(g) \rightarrow N_2(g) + 2H_2O(l)$;
   b $N_2O(g) + NO_2(g) \rightarrow 3NO(g)$

3 When excess zinc is added to 50 cm³ of 1.00 mol dm⁻³ copper sulfate solution, a temperature change of 50.5 °C is obtained.
   a Write the equation for the reaction.   b Calculate the enthalpy change for the reaction.
   c Calculate the standard enthalpy change for the reaction.

UNIT 2

Reaction rates

Collision theory

This theory states that:

- particles must collide in order to react
- for a successful reaction, the collision must be energetic enough to overcome the **activation energy** (the minimum energy needed for reaction to occur)
- for a successful reaction, the particles must be in correct orientation to each other.

We use collision theory to explain the effects of the following factors on reaction rate.

Concentration

An increase in the *concentration* of a solution or the *pressure* of a gas increases the reaction rate.

Explanation:

If the concentration of a solution or the pressure of a gas is increased, there are more particles present in the same volume.

This means there will be more frequent collisions, so the proportion of collisions that have the required energy (the **activation energy**, E_a) is increased.

Temperature

An increase in temperature increases the reaction rate.

Explanation:

If the temperature is increased, the particles move more quickly.

This means there will be more frequent collisions, so the proportion of collisions that have the required energy (the **activation energy** E_a) is increased.

However, the more important reason is that the collisions are *more efficient* because the particles have a greater average energy, therefore more collisions have energies greater than the activation energy, making reaction more likely.

✔ *Quick check 2*

The Boltzmann distribution

In a sample of gas, the particles have different speeds. This means they also have different energies. The Boltzmann distribution shows us the distribution of the molecular energies in a sample of gas.

If the temperature is increased, the distribution alters – the maximum of the curve is lower and moves to the right. This shows that the number of molecules possessing at least the activation energy is greater, so the reaction rate increases.

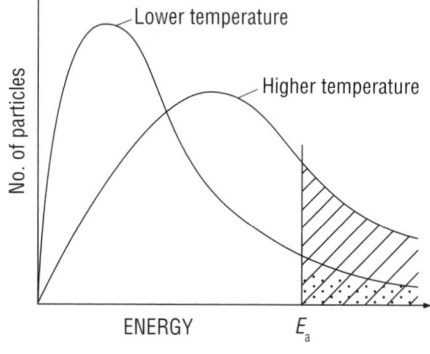

✔ *Quick check 3*

Catalysts

A **catalyst** is a substance that enters into the reaction and increases the reaction rate, without being changed or consumed by the reaction.

Example:
Chlorine (Cl•) radicals from chlorofluorocarbons break down ozone in the ozone layer by the following reactions:

$$Cl• + O \rightarrow ClO•$$

$$ClO• + O_3 \rightarrow Cl• + 2O_2$$

The overall reaction is $O + O_3 \rightarrow 2O_2$ and the Cl• is regenerated and is unchanged. Therefore it is a catalyst.

- It provides an alternative reaction pathway of lower **activation energy**. This is shown by the enthalpy profile diagram to the right:

Catalysts also save energy because they lower the activation energy, so the reacting particles need less energy to react; lower temperatures are possible. This can be seen in the Boltzmann distribution in the figure below right.

Catalysts have great economic importance. Major areas in which they are used include:

- fertiliser production – iron is used in the production of ammonia, the major feedstock for fertilisers

- margarine production – nickel is used in the hydrogenation of unsaturated oils

- petroleum and plastics production

- reducing pollution – the catalytic converter in cars uses a catalyst of platinum/rhodium/palladium.

Enzymes are biological catalysts – they are proteins, and are much more specific than inorganic catalysts. They work at the temperature of the organism, which is often close to room temperature. They have a lot of large-scale uses, including brewing, bread and food production and drug production.

Hint

For the catalysed reaction, the number of molecules with sufficient energy to react (indicated by the shaded area) increases.

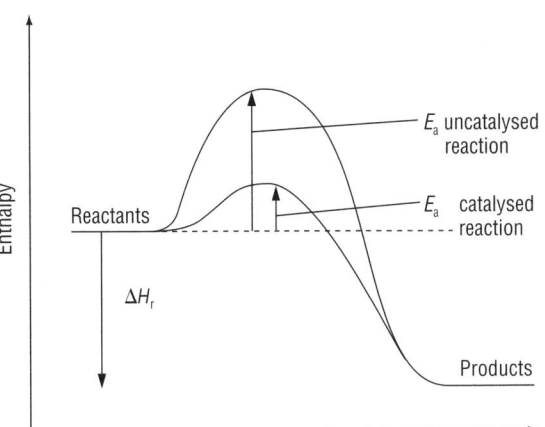

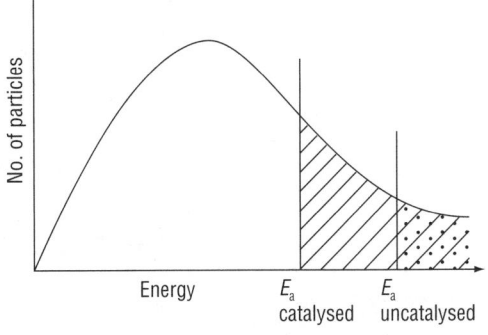

Module 3

✓ *Quick check 4*

QUICK CHECK QUESTIONS

1 Sketch an enthalpy profile diagram for the combustion of methane, labelling the reactants, the products, the activation energy and enthalpy change of reaction.

2 When solid zinc granules are added to sulfuric acid, the following reaction takes place:

$$Zn(s) + H_2SO_4(g) \rightarrow ZnSO_4(aq) + H_2(g)$$

Give four ways of increasing the rate of the reaction.

3 Draw a Boltzmann distribution of gas molecules and use it to show that raising the temperature increases the rate of reaction.

4 The reaction between I^- ions and $S_2O_8^{2-}$ ions ($2I^- + S_2O_8^{2-} \rightarrow I_2 + 2SO_4^{2-}$) is slow. The reaction is catalysed by Fe^{2+} ions as follows:

$$2Fe^{2+} + S_2O_8^{2-} \rightarrow 2SO_4^{2-} + 2Fe^{3+}$$
$$2Fe^{3+} + 2I^- \rightarrow 2Fe^{2+} + I_2$$

Explain why the Fe^{2+} ion is a catalyst for this reaction.

Chemical equilibrium

Key words

- equilibrium
- closed system
- dynamic
- le Chatelier
- reversible

An equilibrium is two opposing processes taking place *at equal rates*.

We use the symbol $\rightleftharpoons$ to show this:

$2NO_2(g) \rightleftharpoons N_2O_4(g)$ means that when a steady state has been reached, nitrogen dioxide (NO_2) is constantly changing to dinitrogen tetroxide (N_2O_4), which is changing back again at the same rate.

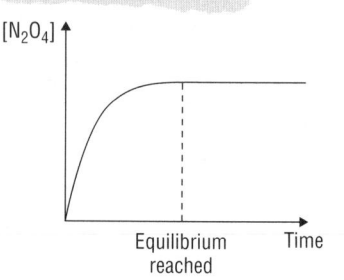

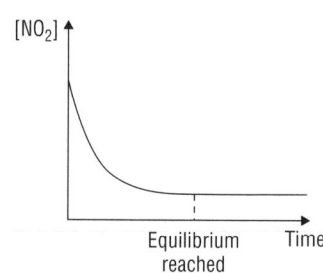

The steady state is important. If you started with just NO_2, it would take some time before N_2O_4 was formed and equilibrium was established.

Dynamic equilibrium

A dynamic equilibrium:

- takes place in a closed system (no exchange of matter with the surroundings)
- has forward and reverse reactions with equal rates
- has constancy of macroscopic properties such as temperature, pressure and concentration – it looks as if the system is not changing, but at the molecular level the forward and reverse reactions are occurring constantly.

le Chatelier's principle

Examiner tip

Catalysts do not affect the equilibrium. They only speed up the rate at which equilibrium is reached.

✓ *Quick check 1 and 2*

- When a system in a dynamic equilibrium is subject to a change the position of equilibrium will shift to minimise the change.

You must be able to explain what happens to an equilibrium with:

- a change in concentration (aqueous reactions) or pressure (gaseous reactions)
- a change in temperature.

These changes are summarised below by looking at the reaction

$PCl_5(g) \rightleftharpoons PCl_3(g) + Cl_2(g)$ where the forward reaction is endothermic.

Condition	Effect on position of equilibrium	Example
Increase in pressure (gaseous)	The equilibrium will shift to the side of the reaction that gives fewer gas molecules and the pressure is reduced	Example: $PCl_5(g) \rightleftharpoons PCl_3(g) + Cl_2(g)$. In this reaction there is 1 mole of gas on the left and 2 moles of gas on the right. If the pressure is *increased* the reaction moves to the *left* to form fewer gas molecules and hence give a reduced pressure
Decrease in pressure	The equilibrium will shift to the side of the reaction that gives more gas molecules and the pressure is increased	

Condition	Effect on position of equilibrium	Example
Increase in temperature	The endothermic reaction is favoured, as this will lower the temperature and oppose the change	Example: $PCl_5(g) \rightleftharpoons PCl_3(g) + Cl_2(g)$ The *forward reaction* is *endothermic* and is therefore favoured by an increase in temperature. Raising the temperature means the reaction moves to the *right*
Decrease in temperature	The exothermic reaction is favoured, as this will raise the temperature and oppose the change	
Increase in concentration of product	The backward reaction (formation of reactants) is favoured, as this will lower the concentration of the product and oppose the change	Example $PCl_5(g) \rightleftharpoons PCl_3(g) + Cl_2(g)$ If the concentration of $PCl_3(g)$ *increases*, the equilibrium shifts to the *left* in order to reduce the concentration
Increase in concentration of reactant	The forward reaction (formation of products) is favoured, as this will lower the concentration of the reactant	

Compromises between yield (chemical equilibrium) and reaction rate

In industry, chemists have to find a balance between conditions that favour a good yield of the desired products, but at the same time give the quickest reaction rate. A good illustration of this is the Haber process to produce ammonia.

The equation for this exothermic reaction is as follows:

$$N_2(g) + 3H_2(g) \rightleftharpoons 2NH_3(g) \quad \Delta H_r^{\ominus} = -92\,kJ\,mol^{-1}$$

The effects of the various conditions on yield and rate and the compromises reached are summarised below.

✔**Quick check 3**

Condition	Conditions that favour high yield of ammonia	Effect of conditions on rate	Compromises and reasons
Pressure	High pressure favours the formation of fewer gas molecules, i.e. more ammonia	Increases rate as it pushes molecules together, increasing their concentration	200 atmospheres – much higher pressures need a lot more energy and expensive machinery; also safety problems
Temperature	Low temperature	Decreases rate because fewer molecules have sufficient energy to react	450 °C – yield is sacrificed for a faster rate at higher temperature; these conditions give about 15% yield of ammonia
Catalyst	No effect on equilibrium	Increases rate	Iron catalyst – saves energy as well as increasing the rate

QUICK CHECK QUESTIONS

1 In the following equilibria, state the effect of increasing the pressure:
   a $COCl_2(g) \rightleftharpoons CO(g) + Cl_2(g)$
   b $CS_2(g) + 4H_2(g) \rightleftharpoons CH_4(g) + 2H_2S(g)$
   c $4NH_3(g) + 5O_2(g) \rightleftharpoons 4NO(g) + 6H_2O(g)$
   d $H_2(g) + I_2(g) \rightleftharpoons 2HI(g)$

2 The gas nitrogen dioxide dimerises:

   $2NO_2(g) \rightleftharpoons N_2O_4(g) \quad \Delta H = -54\,kJ\,mol^{-1}$

   Explain why the amount of nitrogen dioxide is increased when the temperature of this equilibrium is increased.

3 *Syngas*, $CO(g)$ and $H_2(g)$ is produced by the *endothermic* reaction between methane and water. The equation is as follows:

   $CH_4(g) + H_2O(g) \rightleftharpoons CO(g) + 3H_2(g)$

   The conditions used are 850 °C and a pressure of 10–20 atmospheres. What are the best conditions for a good equilibrium yield, and what compromises are made?

The greenhouse effect and global warming

Key words

- greenhouse
- factor
- global warming
- carbon 'sink'

You will have studied this topic at GCSE level, and you should be familiar with terms such as greenhouse effect and global warming.

What is the greenhouse effect?

- The warming of the Earth's surface by infrared radiation that is absorbed by gases and then re-emitted is called the **greenhouse effect**.

- If it wasn't for this warming effect, the Earth's average temperature would be about 30 K less than it is now.

- A steady-state system exists in which the rate at which the Earth absorbs energy is equal to the rate at which energy is radiated back into space.

Greenhouse gases

- A greenhouse gas is one that lets the Sun's radiation through, but prevents infrared radiation leaving.

- All greenhouse gases contain chemical bonds that absorb infrared radiation, making these bonds bend, stretch and vibrate. The bonds that absorb the radiation include the C=O, O–H and C–H bonds.

✓*Quick check 1*

- The ability of a gas to absorb infrared radiation is called its greenhouse factor. The greenhouse factors for all these gases are measured against carbon dioxide (CO_2), which is given a greenhouse factor of 1.

- The contribution of a gas to the greenhouse effect depends on its greenhouse factor and its atmospheric concentration (measured in parts per million by volume, ppmv). Data on various gases, excluding water vapour, are given in the table below.

Gas		Greenhouse factor	Concentration/ppmv	Overall contribution to greenhouse effect/%
CO_2		1	368	72.4
CH_4		30	1.7	7.2
N_2O		150	0.3	19
CFCs and other gases	CF_2Cl_2	6650	0.027	1.43
	CCl_3F	1320		

- As can be seen from the table, CO_2 makes the greatest contribution to the greenhouse effect (apart from water vapour).

Global warming

- For the past 150 years, increased burning of fossil fuels, deforestation and other human activities have increased the concentration of atmospheric CO_2, which has been accompanied by an accelerating rise in atmospheric temperature.

- Many scientists believe that the accelerated warming could lead to disaster as the Earth's ecosystems may not be able to adapt.

How is CO_2 removed from the atmosphere?

Carbon 'sinks' are natural ways of removing CO_2 from the air and trapping it.

- Plants remove CO_2 by photosynthesis. In the oceans, phytoplankton use dissolved CO_2 in this process.
- CO_2 reacts with water, hence the seas can act as atmospheric sinks.
- CO_2 is converted into calcium carbonate by zooplankton in the oceans. When these die, they sink to the bottom of the ocean, thus removing the CO_2.

What are the possible consequences of global warming?

- Melting of the polar ice caps is likely to lead to a rise in sea levels and the consequent disappearance of huge areas of land inhabited by humans.
- When CO_2 dissolves in water, an acidic solution is formed. This acidification of the oceans could dissolve calcium carbonate on coral reefs. ✔*Quick check 2*
- Higher temperatures lead to more severe storms and more frequent extremes of weather. The intensity of hurricanes in the Gulf of Mexico has increased in recent years, for example.
- Climate changes lead to desertification of arid regions.

How can the emissions of CO_2 be reduced?

1 Reduce the use of fossil fuels for energy production. Chemists are developing fuels extracted from renewable sources, known as biofuels, and there has been an increase in the use of fuels such as ethanol as alternatives to petrol.
2 In the future, carbon capture and storage (CCS) could reduce CO_2 emissions by power plants by as much as 90%. ✔*Quick check 3*

- The CO_2 emitted by power stations is separated from other gases, compressed and then pumped under pressure into deep geological formations, including saline formations, exhausted gas or oil fields, and unminable coal seams. The CO_2 is adsorbed onto the coal surface.
- Other sites for storage include ocean storage.
- The CO_2 could also be reacted with metal oxides to form stable, solid metal carbonates.

$$MO(s) + CO_2(g) \longrightarrow MCO_3(s)$$
metal oxide   metal carbonate

- CO_2 can be reacted with slurries of metal carbonates in water. For example, calcium carbonate from limestone reacts with CO_2 to form a solution of soluble calcium hydrogencarbonate, which can then be disposed of by releasing below the ocean surface.

Module 4

QUICK CHECK QUESTIONS

1 a Explain the term 'greenhouse factor'.
   b Why does carbon dioxide contribute more than methane to global warming, even though it has a lower greenhouse factor?

2 a Explain why CO_2 dissolving in water leads to acidification.
   b Why are coral reefs affected by this acidification?

3 List the ways that CO_2 can be removed from the atmosphere by carbon capture and storage.

UNIT 2

Atmospheric pollution

Key words

- ultraviolet
- ozone
- radical
- catalyst
- chlorofluorocarbons
- catalytic converter
- pollutant
- greenhouse gas

Hint

The * means 'has extra energy'. M is another gas molecule that can take away the energy produced in the reaction.

✔ *Quick check 1*

✔ *Quick check 1 and 2*

✔ *Quick check 3*

Module 4

The ozone layer and its depletion

- On the Earth's surface, ozone is toxic, and reacts with unburned hydrocarbons from cars to give carcinogens and irritants. In some conditions, the chemicals form a photochemical smog.

- In the stratosphere (10–50 km above the Earth's surface) ozone absorbs harmful ultraviolet rays from the Sun. The reactions responsible are:

$$\text{(A) } O_3 \xrightarrow[\text{M}]{\text{UV radiation}} O_2(g) + O^*$$

$$\text{(B) } O_2(g) + O^* \xrightarrow{\text{M}} O_3(g)$$

- Reactions (A) and (B) maintain a steady state in the stratosphere, so, if undisturbed, ozone would maintain a protective layer around the Earth.

- If the ozone layer did not protect the Earth's surface by absorbing UV radiation, the UV would cause an increase in skin cancer and cataracts in humans, and harm many living organisms.

- It is now firmly established that the ozone layer has been substantially depleted, especially around the poles (up to 70% in the Antarctic). In more temperate zones, such as the UK, this depletion is around 15%.

- One group of chemicals responsible for this depletion is chlorofluorocarbons (CFCs). These produce chlorine radicals ($Cl\bullet$), which catalyse the breakdown of ozone (see below).

- At the high temperatures reached in jet engines and thunderstorms, there is sufficient energy to break the $N \equiv N$ bond in N_2; the nitrogen can then react with oxygen to form oxides of nitrogen, e.g. $N_2 + O_2 \rightarrow 2NO\bullet$

Catalytic radical	$NO\bullet(g)$	$Cl\bullet(g)$
Source of catalyst	Reaction between oxygen and nitrogen at high temperatures (in aircraft engines and thunderstorms)	From CFCs such as CF_2Cl_2, which dissociate in the stratosphere: $CCl_2F_2 \rightarrow CF_2Cl\bullet + Cl\bullet$
How does the catalyst work?	$NO\bullet$ radical reacts with ozone: $NO\bullet(g) + O_3(g) \rightarrow NO_2(g) + O_2(g)$ $NO\bullet$ is regenerated by the NO_2 reacting with O atoms: $NO_2(g) + O(g) \rightarrow NO\bullet + O_2(g)$	$Cl\bullet$ radical reacts with ozone: $Cl\bullet(g) + O_3(g) \rightarrow ClO\bullet(g) + O_2(g)$ $Cl\bullet$ is regenerated by the $ClO\bullet$ reacting with O atoms: $ClO\bullet(g) + O(g) \rightarrow Cl\bullet + O_2(g)$
Overall reaction	$O_3(g) + O(g) \rightarrow 2O_2(g)$ $Cl\bullet$ and $NO\bullet$ radicals speed up this reaction and are regenerated at the end, therefore they are catalysts One CFC molecule can lead to the destruction of 100 000 ozone molecules	

The Montreal Protocol (1989) banned CFCs for such uses as refrigerants and fire extinguishers. They were replaced by hydrofluorocarbons (HFCs), which have fewer damaging effects. It takes about 17 years for a CFC molecule to reach the stratosphere, where it can survive for up to 100 years, so the effects of CFCs will last for a long time yet.

Car emissions and catalytic converters

- We depend on the internal combustion engine. Unfortunately, it is a major polluter.

- **Catalytic converters** remove many pollutants from exhaust gases.

- They consist of a cylindrical structure containing a ceramic honeycomb with a large surface area coated with a solid catalyst – a mixture of platinum, palladium and rhodium (see page 77). Hot exhaust gases are mixed with air and pass through the catalytic converter.

- The reactants form weak bonds with the catalyst surface (**adsorption**; **desorption** is when the products leave the surface). The catalyst is chosen so that:
  the bonds formed are weak enough for adsorption and desorption to take place
  the bonds formed are strong enough to weaken bonds in the pollutant molecules so a reaction can take place.

✓ *Quick check 4*

- The catalytic converter converts hydrocarbons and carbon monoxide (CO) to carbon dioxide (CO_2) and H_2O. This is not a complete answer to the problem, as CO_2 is a **greenhouse gas** that accumulates in the upper atmosphere, preventing heat loss from the Earth and causing global warming.

- There are two types of converter:
  oxidation catalysts for diesel engines – the pollutants react with oxygen on the catalyst surface
  three-way catalysts for petrol engines – the pollutants react together on the catalyst surface.

	Hydrocarbons	Carbon monoxide (CO)	Oxides of nitrogen (NO, NO_2, N_2O, etc.)
Where does it come from?	Not all fuel (petrol or diesel) burns in the engine – some escapes unchanged	CO is formed when hydrocarbons burn inefficiently, with insufficient oxygen. For example: $C_8H_{18} + 9\frac{1}{2}\,O_2 \rightarrow 8CO + 9H_2O$	At the high temperatures reached in the car engine and exhaust, the $N{\equiv}N$ breaks and the nitrogen reacts with oxygen to form oxides of nitrogen, or NO_x, such as NO: $N_2 + O_2 \rightarrow 2NO$
What effect does the pollutant have?	Hydrocarbons are toxic and carcinogenic	Carbon monoxide is highly toxic. It combines with haemoglobin in the blood more efficiently than oxygen, and so prevents oxygen reaching the tissues.	Nitrogen oxides have three main effects: (1) They cause *smog*, which is corrosive and irritating to the respiratory tract. It may increase the incidence of asthma. (2) They create low-level *ozone*, also in smog. (3) They contribute to *acid rain*. ✓ *Quick check 5*
What does the catalytic converter do to solve the problem?	It oxidises hydrocarbons to carbon dioxide and water	Three-way converters oxidise CO to CO_2 **step 1: ad**sorption of CO onto active sites on the catalyst **step 2:** reaction with NO **step 3: de**sorption of CO_2 from the catalyst surface	Three-way converters reduce oxides of nitrogen to nitrogen, N_2 **step 1: ad**sorption of NO onto active sites on the catalyst surface **step 2:** chemical reaction with CO **step 3: de**sorption of N_2 from the catalyst surface
What overall reactions occur on the catalyst surface?	On the surface of oxidation converters: $CO + \frac{1}{2}O_2 \rightarrow CO_2$ $C_8H_{18} + 12\frac{1}{2}O_2 \rightarrow 8CO_2 + 9H_2O$ On the surface of three-way converters: $2CO + 2NO \rightarrow N_2 + 2CO_2$		✓ *Quick check 6*

Module 4

QUICK CHECK QUESTIONS

1 a What chemicals are produced by the dissociation of CFCs in the stratosphere?

   b What chemicals are produced by the reaction of nitrogen and oxygen? Why are these chemicals produced in jet engines and thunderstorms?

2 a Give the equations that show how chemicals formed from CFCs break down the ozone layer.

   b Give the equations that show how NO• leads to depletion of the ozone layer.

   c Why are NO• radicals regarded as catalysts in this process?

3 The bond energies for the C–F and C–Cl bonds are $467\,kJ\,mol^{-1}$ and $346\,kJ\,mol^{-1}$, respectively. In terms of reducing damage to the ozone layer, why do you think HFCs are preferable to CFCs?

4 Why are the metals used in catalytic converters chosen carefully?

5 Vehicle exhausts emit the pollutant nitrogen monoxide. Describe *one* effect of this pollutant, and explain how its emission can be controlled.

6 a Name the two main types of catalytic converter.

   b Give the equations for the reactions taking place in catalytic converters used in diesel vehicles.

   c Give the equation for the reaction taking place in catalytic converters used in petrol vehicles.

Green chemistry and sustainability

✓*Quick check 1*

Chemists need to design chemical processes that do not pollute the environment, that produce as little waste as possible, and that are based on chemicals that will not run out. What are the criteria for a green, sustainable chemical industry?

- Chemical processes have to produce a good **percentage yield** of product and have a good **atom economy**. Remember:

$$\text{percentage yield} = \left(\frac{\text{actual yield}}{\text{theoretical yield}}\right) \times 100$$

$$\text{atom economy} = \left(\frac{\text{molecular mass of desired product}}{\text{sum of molecular masses of all products}}\right) \times 100$$

- A good yield means that we produce as much as possible of the desired product.
- A good atom economy means that there are as few waste products as possible. It is better to prevent waste than to have to treat it or clean it up.
- The impact on the environment should be as small as possible – the process should not deplete the Earth's resources, and the products formed should not harm the environment.

How can these criteria be satisfied?

- Reactions with a high atom economy (**addition reactions**) should be chosen over those with a lower one (e.g. **substitution reactions**).
- Chemical processes should use renewable resources wherever possible, such as chemicals derived from plant material.
- All reactants and products should be evaluated for their toxicity.
- The number of steps in a process should be kept to a minimum. This minimises the production of waste materials and increases the overall percentage yield. Three steps in a process, each with a 90% yield, give an overall yield of $(0.9)^3 \times 100 = 73\%$. Six steps with the same yield give a final yield of $(0.9)^6 \times 100 = 53\%$.
- Catalysts should be used wherever possible. They make reactions with improved atom economy possible. They also improve the yield at a given temperature and save energy because they enable reactions to take place at lower temperatures.
- Solvents can be chosen to be more environmentally friendly.

✓*Quick check 2*

Hint

Organic solvents are sometimes significant pollutants. Chemists are trying to replace them with water, carbon dioxide and ionic liquids. CO_2 has been developed as a solvent for dry-cleaning clothes.

Hint

In the Boots process, for 3 million kg of ibuprofen the amount of waste products is 4.5 million kg.

Synthesis of ibuprofen – an exercise in green chemistry

Ibuprofen is a much-used painkiller. Around 3 million kg of the chemical are consumed per year in the UK alone.

Two processes are compared in the table below, along with the advantages of the 'greener' BHC process over the Boots process.

Factor	Boots process	BHC process	Improvement
Number of steps	6	3	Fewer steps facilitates higher yield.
Use of catalysts	Only three of the six steps use catalysts. One of these catalysts, $AlCl_3$, is gradually converted to $Al(OH)_3$ and has to be stored on waste sites. This is a 'false catalyst' as it is changed by the reaction.	All three steps use a catalyst. There are no 'false catalysts'. Two of the catalysts are **heterogeneous**, so they can easily be separated from reactants and products.	Catalysts save energy and make possible reactions that have a higher atom economy.
Atom economy	Every step has waste products. The overall atom economy is 40%.	The overall atom economy is 77% and the one waste product, ethanoic acid, can be used in other processes.	Much less waste. Also, to obtain the desired output, lower amounts of reactants are needed.
Types of reaction	Every reaction produces unwanted products.	Two out of three of the reactions are **addition reactions** and therefore have a 100% atom economy.	Incorporation of more desirable addition reactions.

What are greener alternatives to fossil fuels?

Ethanol and methanol can both be used as car fuels or as additives. They are both renewable, as they can be derived from plant materials and 'cleaner' fuels than petrol.

Biodiesel is an alternative to ordinary diesel. It is extracted from rapeseed and sunflower oils. It is biodegradable and produces fewer toxic particulates.

The role of international agreements in a greener economy

Agreement	Beneficial effects
Rio (1992)	Emphasises sustainable development and assessment of environmental impact.
Kyoto (1997)	Sets limits to production of greenhouse gases in order to slow down global warming.
Montreal (1989)	Bans use of CFCs in order to slow down depletion of ozone layer.

✔ *Quick check 3 and 4*

✔ *Quick check 5*

Module 4

Hint

One problem with planting crops to produce biodiesel is that land used for this cannot be used for conventional food crops.

QUICK CHECK QUESTIONS

1 What is the atom economy of the following reactions?
   a $CH_3CH_2OH + NaBr + H_2SO_4 \rightarrow CH_3CH_2Br + NaHSO_4 + H_2O$ to produce (CH_3CH_2Br)
   b $H_2C=CH_2 + \frac{1}{2}O_2 \rightarrow (CH_2)_2O$

2 What is the overall percentage yield for a process involving two steps, each step giving 60% yield?

3 In the Boots process, why is $AlCl_3$ a false catalyst?

4 Explain one advantage and one disadvantage of biodiesel as an alternative fuel.

5 Briefly list the reasons why the BHC process for making ibuprofen is better than the Boots process.

UNIT 2

End-of-unit questions

1 The diagrams below show the structures of four isomers of molecular formula C_4H_8.

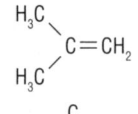

A   B   C   D

- **a** **i** To which class of compounds do the four isomers belong? (1)
- **ii** Which two diagrams show compounds that are *E–Z* isomers? (2)
- **b** **i** Which of these compounds could be formed from 2-methylpropan-2-ol by the elimination of water? (1)
- **ii** State the reagents and conditions by which this reaction could be carried out in the laboratory (2)

2 Samples of butan-1-ol, butan-2-ol and 2-methylpropan-2-ol were reacted with aqueous acidified potassium dichromate(VI). Complete the table below for each of the three alcohols. State what you would observe, and identify the organic product of each reaction. (6)

Alcohol	Observation	Organic product (if any)
butan-1-ol		
butan-2-ol		
2-methylpropan-2-ol		

3 An important use of chlorine is in the production of plastics such as polychloroethene (PVC).
The monomer is shown below.

- **a** Draw the displayed formula for the repeat unit of PVC. (1)
- **b** State **two** problems that arise from the disposal of PVC. (2)

4 Explain the following reaction terms as used in organic chemistry. In each case, give **one** example reaction. For each example, name the reactants, state the conditions, name the organic product(s) and give an equation.
- **a** Electrophilic addition. *eg. propene + bromine* (4)
- **b** Elimination. *eg. ethanol → ethene* (4)
- **c** Nucleophilic substitution. *eg. bromoethane → ethanol* (4)

5 Cracking of the unbranched compound **E**, C_6H_{14}, produced the saturated compound **F** and an unsaturated hydrocarbon **G** (M_r 42). Compound **E** reacted with bromine in UV radiation to form a monobrominated compound **H** and an acidic gas **I**. Compound **G** reacted with hydrogen bromide to form a mixture of two compounds, **J** and **K**.
- **a** Use this evidence to suggest the identity of each of compounds **E** to **K**. Include equations for the reactions in your answer. (10)
- **b** Oil companies often change the structures of compounds such as **E**. Explain why this is done, and suggest **two** organic products of changing the structures of **E** by dehydrogenation (removal of hydrogen). (3)
- **c** Predict the structure of the polymer that could be formed from compound **G**. (1)

6 Petrol and camping gas are examples of fuels that contain hydrocarbons.

    a Petrol is a mixture of alkanes containing 6–10 carbon atoms per molecule. Some of these alkanes are isomers of one another.

        i Explain the term 'isomer'.   (1)

        ii State the molecular formula of an alkane present in petrol.   (1)

    b The major hydrocarbon in camping gas is butane. Some camping gas was reacted with chlorine to form a mixture of isomers.

        i What conditions are required for this reaction to take place?   (2)

        ii Two isomers, **A** and **B**, were separated from this mixture. These isomers had a molar mass of $92.5\,g\,mol^{-1}$. Deduce the molecular formulae of these two isomers.   (2)

        iii Draw the displayed formulae of **A** and **B** and name each compound.   (2)

X 7 a Sketch the reaction pathway for an exothermic process on an enthalpy profile diagram. On your diagram, label:

        i the enthalpy change of reaction, ΔH

        ii the activation energy of the reaction, E_a.   (3)

    b **i** Sketch the distribution of energies of the molecules of a gas at temperature T_1. Label this line T_1.

        ii On the same axes, sketch the distribution of energies of the molecules of the gas at a higher temperature, T_2. Label this line T_2.

        iii Use your sketches to explain how a higher temperature affects the rate of a reaction.   (7)

8 Production of methane as biogas is growing rapidly as an alternative energy supply, particularly in some countries. Methane can be used as a fuel because of its exothermic reaction with oxygen.

$$CH_4(g) + 2O_2(g) \rightarrow CO_2(g) + 2H_2O(l) \quad \Delta H^{\ominus}_c(CH_4(g)) = -890.3\,kJ\,mol^{-1}$$

    a Explain what is meant by $\Delta H^{\ominus}_c(CH_4(g)) = -890.3\,kJ\,mol^{-1}$.   (3)

    b The enthalpy change of formation of methane, $\Delta H^{\ominus}_f(CH_4(g))$, cannot be measured directly.

        i Using the data below, calculate the enthalpy change of formation of methane.

$$C(s) + 2H_2(g) \rightarrow CH_4(g)$$

Compound	$\Delta H^{\ominus}_c/kJ\,mol^{-1}$
$CH_4(g)$	–890.3
$C(s)$	–393.5
$H_2(g)$	–285.9

        ii Suggest why the enthalpy change of formation of methane cannot be measured directly.   (4)

    c A typical biogas plant in China, using the dung from five cows, can produce $3000\,dm^3$ of biogas a day. The biogas contains 60% of methane by volume. Using these data, calculate the maximum heat energy that can be produced each day from the methane in the biogas. (Assume 1 mole of methane occupies $24\,dm^3$ under these conditions.)   (3)

9 The important gas ammonia (NH_3) is produced on an industrial scale by the exothermic reaction between nitrogen and hydrogen.

   a Give the equation for the reaction. (1)

        The conditions used are as follows:

        I   25 MPa

        II   450°C

        III iron catalyst.

   b **i**   Define standard conditions. (3)

      ii Explain the conditions used, and explain how they are a compromise between getting a good yield and a high rate of production. (12)

   c Iron is a catalyst in this reaction. Explain the term 'catalyst'. (3)

   d The bond enthalpies of the bonds involved in the reaction are shown below:

        $N\equiv N(g)$ 945 kJ mol^{-1}; $H-H(g)$ 436 kJ mol^{-1}; $N-H$ 391 kJ mol^{-1} (g).

        Using these bond enthalpies, calculate the standard enthalpy of reaction for the production of ammonia. (3)

10 The ozone layer is a protective layer of gas in the stratosphere circling the Earth.

   a **i**   Give the formula for ozone. (1)

      ii With the aid of a chemical equation, explain how ozone can protect the Earth's surface from ultraviolet radiation. (3)

   b Another reaction taking place in the stratosphere is shown in the following equation:

        $O_3(g) + O^* \rightarrow 2O_2(g)$ $\Delta H = -390$ kJ mol^{-1}

        Explain the effect of this reaction on the temperature of the stratosphere. (2)

   c Explain the consequences of the depletion of the ozone layer by various chemicals. (2)

   d Give equations to show how the NO• radical causes the breakdown of the ozone layer. (4)

   e **i**   Give the advantages of using three rather than six steps in a synthetic process. (2)

      ii If the percentage yield of a process involving three steps is 50% for each step, what is the **overall** percentage yield for the process? (2)

OVERALL 107 MARKS

Answers to quick check questions

Unit 1 Atoms, Bonds and Groups
Module 1 – Atoms and reactions
Atoms, molecules and stoichiometry
1 a 20p, 20e, 20n   b 8p, 8e, 8n
  c 6p, 6e, 8n
2 a 10e   b 10e
  c 10e
3 a $Ca(OH)_2$ b $Pb_3(PO_4)_2$
  c $BaCO_3$ d K_2SO_4
  e $Fe(OH)_3$
4 a $N_2 + 3H_2 \rightarrow 2NH_3$ b $3Fe + 4H_2O \rightarrow Fe_3O_4 + 4H_2$
  c $Na_2O + H_2O \rightarrow 2NaOH$ d $PCl_5 + 4H_2O \rightarrow H_3PO_4 + 5HCl$
5 a $2Br^- + Cl_2 \rightarrow Br_2 + 2Cl^-$ b $Mg + 2H^+ \rightarrow H_2 + Mg^{2+}$.
6 a $Mg(s) + H_2SO_4(aq) \rightarrow MgSO_4(aq) + H_2(g)$
  b $Mg(s) + 2H^+(aq) \rightarrow Mg^{2+}(aq) + H_2(g)$

Isotopes and relative masses
1 a i Both isotopes have 26p and 26e
    ii both isotopes have 36p and 36e
  b i $^{56}_{26}Fe$ has 30n and $^{57}_{26}Fe$ has 31n
    ii $^{78}_{36}Kr$ has 42n and $^{80}_{36}Kr$ has 44n
2 a 40   b 50
  c 65
3 10.8
4 a 95.3   b 100.1
  c 149   d 187.5
  e 342.3

Amount of substance – the mole
1 a 12.04×10^{23} (1.204×10^{24})
  b 60.02×10^{23} (6.02×10^{24})
2 $149.9\,g\,mol^{-1}$
3 0.02 mol
4 0.005 (5×10^{-3}) mol
5 a $4.8\,dm^3$ b 0.06 mol

Types of mole calculation
1 1.40 g
2 0.173 mol
3 $1.2\,dm^3$
4 a 0.025 mol   b 1.34 g
  c 1.39 g   d $0.05\,mol\,dm^{-3}$

Empirical and molecular formulae
1 C_2H_6O
2 Empirical formula $C_6H_{11}O_2$; molecular formula $C_{12}H_{22}O_4$
3 A, Fe_2O_3; B, FeO; C, Fe_3O_4
4 NaO

Acids, bases and salts
1 a $HNO_3(aq) \rightarrow H^+(aq) + NO_3^-(aq)$;
    $H_2SO_4(aq) \rightarrow 2H^+(aq) + SO_4^{2-}(aq)$
  b Acids release $H^+(aq)$ ions in solution.
2 a $KOH(aq) \rightarrow K^+(aq) + OH^-(aq)$;
    $Ca(OH)_2(aq) \rightarrow Ca^{2+}(aq) + 2OH^-(aq)$
  b Alkalis release OH^- ions in solution.
3 a $CaCO_3 + 2HNO_3 \rightarrow Ca(NO_3)_2 + H_2O + CO_2$
  b $ZnCO_3 + H_2SO_4 \rightarrow ZnSO_4 + H_2O + CO_2$
  c $MgCO_3 + 2HCl \rightarrow MgCl_2 + H_2O + CO_2$
    CO_2 is fomed so the reaction mixture effervesces.
4 a $CaO + 2HNO_3 \rightarrow Ca(NO_3)_2 + H_2O$
  b $ZnO + 2HCl \rightarrow ZnCl_2 + H_2O$
  c $2NH_3 + H_2SO_4 \rightarrow (NH_4)_2SO_4$

Water of crystallisation and titration calculations
1 a $Na_2CO_3 \cdot 4H_2O$ b $Na_2CO_3 \cdot 10H_2O$
2 $FeSO_4 \cdot 7H_2O$
3 $0.0609\,mol\,dm^{-3}$
4 $50\,cm^3$

Oxidation and reduction
1 Reduction is:
  the gain of hydrogen (e.g. $Li + \frac{1}{2}H_2 \rightarrow LiH$);
  the loss of oxygen (e.g. $PbO_2 \rightarrow PbO + \frac{1}{2}O_2$);
  the gain of electrons (e.g. $\frac{1}{2}Cl_2 + e^- \rightarrow Cl^-$);
  a decrease in oxidation number (e.g. $\frac{1}{2}Cl_2 + e^- \rightarrow Cl^-$; ON of
  $Cl_2 = 0$; ON of $Cl^- = -1$).
2 a +4   b –3
  c +4
3 a NaCl: Na +1, Cl –1; LiF Li+1, F–1; SrO: Sr +2, 0 – 2
  b $MgBr_2$ Mg +2, Br –1
    NaOH Na +1, O –2, H +1
    $AgNO_3$ Ag +1, N +5, O –2
    Na_2SO_4 Na +1, S +6, O –2
    Cl_2 Cl 0
4 a oxidised ($0 \rightarrow +2$)   b oxidised ($+2 \rightarrow +2.5$)
  c reduced ($+3 \rightarrow -2$)

Module 2 – Electrons, bonding and structure
Ionisation energy
1 Less than $940\,kJ\,mol^{-1}$.
2 See text.
3
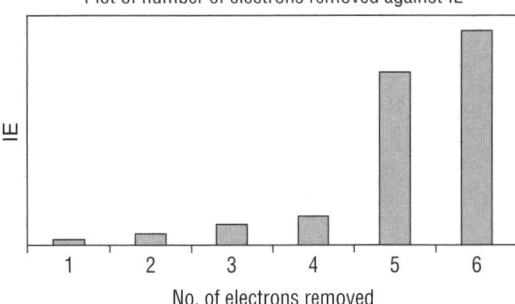

Plot of number of electrons removed against IE

IE (vertical axis) — No. of electrons removed (horizontal axis: 1, 2, 3, 4, 5, 6)

The first four electrons are in the same outer energy level and therefore easier to remove as they are further from attractive pull of the nucleus and are, to some extent, shielded by inner electrons. The fifth electron removed is in an inner energy level, is closer to the nucleus and is not shielded, therefore is much harder to remove, and ionisation energy is very much higher.
4 See text for definition. The three factors are:
- Nuclear charge – the larger the charge on the nucleus, the greater the attraction for electrons and therefore the harder they are to remove. The nuclear charge increases across a period.
- Atomic radius – the greater the atomic radius, the further the outer electrons are from the nucleus and therefore the lower the attractive force on them and the easier they are to remove.
- Electron shielding – the larger the number of complete shells, the more the outer electrons are shielded from the nuclear charge and the easier they are to remove.

Electron configurations – the arrangement of electrons in an atom

1 a $1s^22s^22p^63s^1$ b $1s^22s^22p^63s^23p^64s^23d^3$
   c $1s^22s^22p^63s^23p^6$ d $1s^22s^22p^6$
2 See text.
3 Mg
4 a s-block; b d-block; c p-block.

Chemical bonding

1 a    b

   c

2 a   b

   c   d

3 a   b   c

4 The lone-pair electrons on the ammonia are used to form a dative covalent bond with the boron on the BF_3. The boron has an empty orbital.
5 In covalent bonding, each atom supplies one electron to form the bonding pair. In dative covalent bonding, one of the two bonding atoms supplies both electrons for the bonding electrons.

Shapes of molecules – electron-pair repulsion theory

1 a 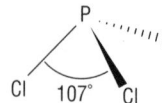   b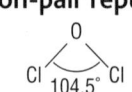

   c 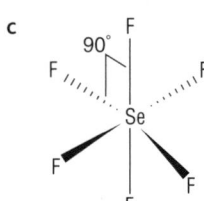   d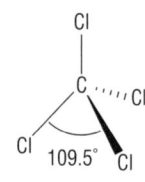

2 a 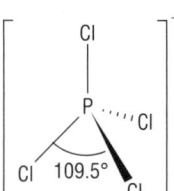   b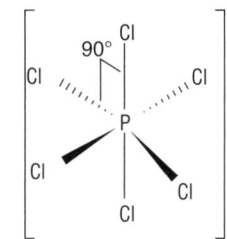

   c 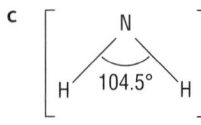   d

3 a Non-linear   b 118–120°.

Electronegativity, polarity and intermolecular forces

1 H–I is polar because there is an asymmetric distribution of charge/electrons (H and I have different electronegativities);

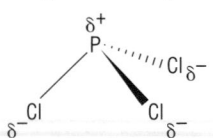

PCl_3 is polar because there is an asymmetric distribution of charge/electrons (P and Cl have different electronegativities);

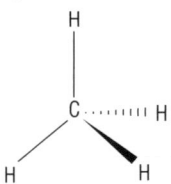

CH_4 is non-polar because the distribution charge/electrons is symmetrical.

2 a C_3H_8 – van der Waals' forces because it is a non-polar molecule.
   b NH_2OH – hydrogen bonding; there are N–H and O–H bonds present in the molecule and therefore there can be hydrogen bonding between the molecules.
   c PCl_3 – dipole–dipole forces because the molecule is polar but there are no N–H or O–H bonds.
3 See diagram on page 60.
4 The ethanol molecule is polar and it contains an O–H bond. Therefore it can form hydrogen bonds between the molecules. The H_3COCH_3 molecule is polar but the bonds' intermolecular forces are dipole–dipole forces and these are weaker than hydrogen bonds, hence the lower boiling point.
5 The intermolecular forces in water are hydrogen bonds whilst in H_2S they are the weaker dipole–dipole forces, and therefore the boiling point of H_2S is much lower than that of H_2O.

Structures and physical properties

1 a Giant ionic   b giant metallic
   c simple molecular (or monatomic)
   d simple molecular.
2 Giant covalent – diamond-type stucture: has a high melting point; very hard; poor electrical conductor.
3 a Simple molecules   b poor
   c poor   d giant molecules
   e giant covalent
   f positive metal ions (cations) and delocalised electrons
   g giant metallic   h high
   i poor   j good
   k giant ionic.

The Periodic Table

1 a Group   b Period.
2 All the elements in the p-block have outermost electrons in a p sub-shell.
3 A, $[Kr]5s^2$; B, $[He] 2s^22p^1$; C, $[Ne] 3s^1$; D, $[He] 2s^22p^6$
4 s-block.

The Periodic Table and periodicity in the elements of Periods 2 and 3

1 a Group   b Period.
2 a As the period is crossed from left to right, the atomic radius decreases.
   b See text.
3 See text.

4 **a** The structure of aluminium is giant metallic and the bonding is metallic. Silicon has a giant covalent structure and all of the bonds are covalent bonds. The covalent bonds in aluminium are stronger than the metallic bonds in aluminium and therefore they need more energy to break them and hence a higher melting point.

  b The structure of carbon (diamond) is giant covalent and all of the strong covalent bonds have to be broken before the carbon melts. Nitrogen has a simple molecular structure and to melt nitrogen, the very weak van der Waals' (intermolecular) forces have to be broken. Therefore much less energy is needed to melt nitrogen and hence a much lower melting point.

The Group 2 elements

1 The electrons in their outer shells are delocalised and free to carry current.

2 As the group is descended extra shells of electrons are added, increasing the atomic radius.

3 **a** Both lose outer two electrons when they react; Be's outer electrons are closer to the nucleus and are less shielded, therefore harder to lose and Be reacts more slowly.

  b **i** Very quick/violent reaction; effervescence:
    $Ra + 2H_2O \rightarrow Ra(OH)_2 + H_2$

    ii $2Ra + O_2 \rightarrow 2RaO$; oxidation number of Ra increases from 0 to +2.

4 $MgCO_3 \rightarrow MgO + CO_2$

5 **a** Neutralises acid.

  b $Ca(OH)_2 + 2HNO_3 \rightarrow Ca(NO_3)_2 + 2H_2O$ (neutralisation)

The Group 7 elements

1 I_2 is the larger molecule so has stronger van der Waals' forces/intermolecular forces.

2 $Br_2(aq) + 2I^-(aq) \rightarrow 2Br^-(aq) + I_2(aq)$; cyclohexane turns orange–brown.

Reactions of the halogens

1 **a** +5; $Cl_2(0) \rightarrow Cl^-(-1) + ClO_3^-(+5)$

  b Cl is reduced and oxidised in the same reaction.

2 ClO^- +1; Cl^- −1; ClO_3^- +5

3 See text.

Unit 2 Chains, energy and resources

Module 1 – Basic concepts and hydrocarbons

Formulae and isomerism

1 **a**

  b

2

3 **a**

  b

4

NOTE: On all of these compounds, the hydrogens can be made explicit but $CH_3–$ can often be given instead of a carbon with all three hydrogens present

Naming organic compounds

1 **a** butan-2-ol   **b** 1-chloropropane
  c but-2-ene   **d** 2-bromopropane

2 **a**   **b**

  c   **d**

3 There is only one possible structure.

4 $CH_3—CH_2—CH_2—CH_2—OH$ $CH_3—CH_2—CH—CH_3$
                                                                $\quad\quad\quad\quad\quad\quad\quad\quad\quad\;\; OH$

            butan-1-ol   butan-2-ol

          $(CH_3)_3COH$ $(CH_3)_2CHCH_2OH$

   2-methylpropan-2-ol   2-methylpropan-1-ol

Percentage yield and atom economy

1 9.2 g of ethanol is 0.2 mol (9.2/46)
∴0.2 mol of bromoethane are produced if 100% conversion takes place.
∴0.2 × 108.9 g (M_r of bromoethane is 108.9)
= 21.8 g of bromoethane are produced if 100% conversion takes place.
∴percentage yield = 5.36/21.8 = 24.6%

2 **a** A $CH_3CH_2CH_2Br$ + KOH → $CH_3CH_2CH_2OH$ + KBr
     60   119   × 100%

    Atom economy = 60/(60 + 119) = 33.5%
    B $CH_3CH=CH_2$ + H_2O → $CH_3CH_2CH_2OH$
      60   × 100%   60

    Atom economy = 60/(60) = 100%

   b Method B, as it produces no waste. Better to start reaction that has few unwanted products than having to find uses for the products.

3 See text.

The alkanes and cycloalkanes

1 C_8H_{18}

2 **a** $C_3H_8 + 5O_2 → 3CO_2 + 4H_2O$
   b $C_3H_8 + 3\frac{1}{2}O_2 → 3CO + 4H_2O$

3 **a**

        Butane   Methylpropane

   b **i** Butane ($CH_3CH_2CH_2CH_3$)
       ii It has more points of contact (larger surface area) and therefore the van der Waals' forces between the molecules are stronger.

4 Two CH_3• (methyl) radicals combine to form ethane.
   CH_3• + CH_3• → $H_3C{:}CH_3$ (C_2H_6)

Hydrocarbons as fuels

1 $C_7H_{16} + 11O_2 → 7CO_2 + 8H_2O$. The products are both gases at the very high temperatures of the car engine and these occupy a greater volume than the reactants.

2 **a** Catalytic conversion to branched/cyclic compounds (see text).

3 **a** **i** $C_{12}H_{26} → C_{10}H_{22} + C_2H_4$ **ii** $C_{12}H_{26} → C_8H_{18} + C_4H_8$
   b They ignite prematurely and cause knocking (see text for details).
   c **i**   or   **ii**

The alkenes

1

2 The number of pairs of electrons round each carbon is four. One of these pairs is used in a π-bond and does not contribute to the shape. Therefore the contributory number of electron pairs is three and the shape is trigonal planar with a bond angle of 120 °C.

3 **a** *E/Z* isomerism.
   b The structural formulae are identical but the displayed formulae showing the arrangements of the atoms and bonds in space are different.
   c **i** No. There are two identical groups on the same carbon.
      ii Yes. The CH_3 and the C_2H_5 groups are on different carbons and therefore they can be on the same or opposite sides of the C=C bond.

4 **a**

    E-1,2-dichloroethene   *Z*-1,2-dichloroethene

   b

  E-2,3-dibromobut-2-ene   *Z*-2,3-dibromobut-2-ene

Reactions of the alkenes

1 **a** **i** Conditions = nickel catalyst; heat.
          Product = ethane (CH_3CH_3, C_2H_6).
      ii Conditions = room temperature with HBr
          Product = bromoethane, CH_3CH_2Br.
      iii Conditions = Br_2 in hexane at room temperature (in the dark). Bromine water would be acceptable.
          Product = 1,2-dibromoethane, CH_2BrCH_2Br.
   b **i** Conditions as for (a) (ii). Product = butane, $CH_3CH_2CH_2CH_3$.
      ii Conditions as (a) (ii). Product = 2-bromobutane, $CH_3CHBrCH_2CH_3$.
      iii Conditions as for (a) (iii). Product = 2,3-dibromobutane, $CH_3CHBrCHBrCH_3$.

2 **a** CH_2 **b** C_3H_6;

   c $CH_3CH_2CH_2OH$ and $CH_3CH(OH)CH_3$
   d $CH_3CH_2CH_2Br$ and $CH_3CHBrCH_3$

3 See text for answer.

4 Margarine is produced from oils which have unsaturated chains (contain C=C bonds) on their molecules. Hydrogenation of these oils using a nickel catalyst gives saturated chains (with no double bonds). Animal fats have chains which are mostly already saturated and therefore do not react with hydrogen.

Addition polymerisation

1 **a** **i**

      ii

      iii

      iv

b **i**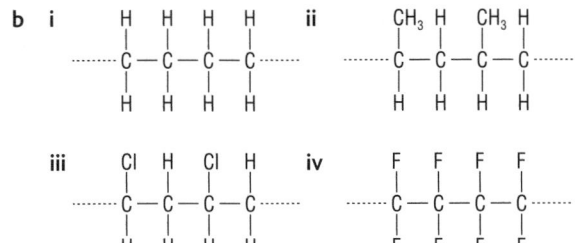

2 **a** Carbon monoxide
b Carbon monoxide, hydrogen chloride and polychlorinated biphenyls
3 **a**

b Carbon monoxide, oxides of nitrogen (NO_x) or more specifically nitrogen dioxide, hydrogen cyanide.

Module 2 – Alcohols, halogenoalkanes and analysis
The alcohols
1 **a** **i** propan-1-ol $CH_3CH_2CH_2OH$;
propan-2-ol $CH_3CH(OH)CH_3$
ii butan-1-ol $CH_3CH_2CH_2CH_2OH$;
butan-2-ol $CH_3CH(OH)CH_2CH_3$
2-methylpropan-1-ol $(CH_3)_2CHCH_2OH$
2-methylpropan-2-ol $(CH_3)_3COH$
b 3-methylbutan-1-ol
2 **a** **i** See text
ii The oxygen in the O–H bond is more electronegative than the hydrogen in this bond, so the electron density on the oxygen is greater.
iii See text
3 **a** $C_3H_7OH + 4\frac{1}{2} O_2 \rightarrow 3CO_2 + 4H_2O$
b They can be produced from plant sources – sugar for ethanol; wood for methanol.
4 **a** propene $CH_3CH=CH_2$
b but-1-ene $CH_3CH_2CH=CH_2$;
but-2-ene (E and Z) $CH_3CH=CHCH_3$
5 **a** $CH_3CH_2OH + CH_3COOH \rightarrow CH_3COOCH_2CH_3 + H_2O$
b $CH_3CH_2CH_2OH + HCOOH \rightarrow HCOOCH_2CH_2CH_3 + H_2O$
c $CH_3OH + CH_3COOH \rightarrow CH_3COOCH_3 + H_2O$

Types of alcohol
1 **a** primary **b** secondary
c primary **d** tertiary
e secondary
2 The ethanol is oxidised to ethanoic acid.
3 Use acidified potassium dichromate(VI) and heat.
The 2-methylpropan-2-ol will have no effect, because it is a tertiary alcohol, and therefore the acidified potassium dichromate stays orange. The butan-2-ol will cause the orange colour to change to greeny-blue because it is oxidised to a ketone, butan-2-one.
4 When the alcohol concentration reaches 15% the yeast is killed and the reaction stops.

The halogenoalkanes
1 **a** C_3H_7Br
b C_3H_7Br
c

2 The isomers are:
$CH_3CH_2CH_2CH_2Br$ 1-bromobutane
$CH_3CHBrCH_2CH_3$ 2-bromobutane
$CH_3CBr(CH_3)CH_3$ 2-bromo-2-methylpropane
$CH_3CH(CH_3)CH_2Br$ 1-bromo-2-methylpropane
3 **a** The synthesis relies on the halogen being replaced by another group and therefore the breaking of the carbon–halogen bond. The C–F bond is very strong and therefore difficult to break, so the reaction would be extremely slow and not viable as part of a synthetic route.
b The C–I bond is too weak and consequently iodoalkanes often react with contaminants before they can be used in a reaction. Bromoalkanes are sufficiently reactive to make them useful in syntheses, but not so reactive that they are unstable or react too easily.

Reactions of the halogenoalkanes
1 The OH^- ion is negative and is therefore attracted to the electron-deficient carbon in the carbon–halogen bond and has a lone pair of electrons which it can donate to the carbon during the reaction.
2 **a** $CH_2BrCH_2Br + 2KOH \rightarrow 2KBr + CH_2OHCH_2OH$
can have $CH_2BrCH_2Br + KOH \rightarrow KBr + CH_2BrCH_2OH$
or $CH_2BrCH_2Br + KOH \rightarrow KBr + CH_2(OH)CH_2Br$
3 Comparable halogenoalkanes such as 1-bromobutane and 1-chlorobutane (both with 4 carbons and both primary halogenoalkanes) are used to make it a fair test.
Silver nitrate solution is dissolved in alcohol and the solution warmed gently (50°C) in two separate test tubes.
Equal amounts of the 1-bromobutane and 1-chlorobutane are added separately to each tube. The appearance of a precipitate indicates the formation of insoluble silver halide.
The speed of the appearance of the precipitate indicates the ease of breaking of the carbon–halogen bond – it is quicker for the 1-bromobutane, indicating that the carbon–bromine bond is the weaker of the two.
4 **a** Easily vaporized/low boiling point and non-corrosive.
b Unreactive and heavy vapours, so will not burn, and sink onto fire, excluding oxygen.
c Good solvents for grease/oil also will evaporate easily so dry quickly.

Infrared spectroscopy
1 **a** –OH group
b alcohol
2 At first the absorption due to the –OH group (at ~ 3400 cm^{-1} the alcohol will disappear as this is oxidised to a carbonyl (C=O) group in the aldehyde. At the same time the absorption at ~1700 cm^{-1} appears and gets stronger.
As the aldehyde is then oxidised to a carboxylic acid a broad absorption at 2500–3300 cm^{-1} appears. The absorption due to the carbonyl group remains.
3 The ethoxyethane has no –OH group and therefore there will be no absorption at ~3400 cm^{-1}.
4 The propan-2-ol will not absorb at ~1700 cm^{-1} because it has no carbonyl (C=O) group.

Mass spectrometry
1 72
2

Peak m/e	Ion responsible	Equation for formation of ion
15	CH_3^+	$CH_3CH_2OH^+ \rightarrow CH_3^+ + \bullet CH_2OH$
29	$CH_3CH_2^+$	$CH_3CH_2OH^+ \rightarrow CH_3CH_2^+ + \bullet OH$
31	CH_2OH^+	$CH_3CH_2OH^+ \rightarrow CH_2OH^+ + \bullet CH_3$

Module 3 – Energy

Enthalpy changes

1 a Exothermic

   b —

   c The chemical system has lost heat energy to the surroundings, therefore enthalpy change **for the system** is negative.

2

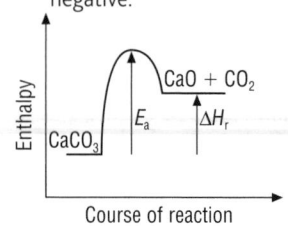

3 a see text   b see text

4

Compound	Equation to represent $\Delta H_f^{\ominus}$	Equation to represent $\Delta H_c^{\ominus}$
$C_2H_6(g)$	$2C(s) + 3H_2(g) \rightarrow C_2H_6(g)$	$C_2H_6(g) + 3\frac{1}{2} O_2 \rightarrow 2CO_2(g) + 3H_2O(l)$
$CO(g)$	$C(s) + \frac{1}{2} O_2(g) \rightarrow CO(g)$	$CO(g) + \frac{1}{2} O_2(g) \rightarrow CO_2(g)$
$CH_3OH(l)$	$C(s) + 2H_2(g) + \frac{1}{2} O_2(g) \rightarrow CH_3OH(l)$	$CH_3OH(l) + 1\frac{1}{2} O_2(g) \rightarrow CO_2(g) + 2H_2O(l)$
$N_2H_4(l)$	$N_2(g) + 2H_2(g) \rightarrow N_2H_4(l)$	$N_2H_4(l) + O_2(g) \rightarrow N_2(g) + 2H_2O(l)$

5 $1173/3 = 391$ kJ mol^{-1}

Calculating enthalpy changes

1 a -1318 kJ mol^{-1} b -212 kJ mol^{-1}

2 a -623 kJ mol^{-1} b $+155$ kJ mol^{-1}

3 a $Zn(s) + CuSO_4(aq) \rightarrow Cu(s) + ZnSO_4(aq)$

   b 10605 J $= 10.6$ kJ

   c -10605 J$/0.05 = -212$ kJ mol^{-1}

Reaction rates

1

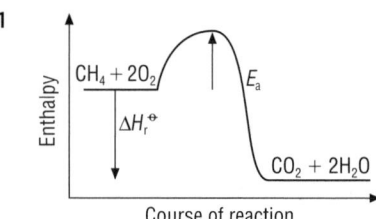

2 a Increasing surface area of the zinc/using zinc powder/using smaller pieces of zinc.
   Increasing the temperature/warming the acid.
   Increasing the concentration of the sulfuric acid solution
   Adding a catalyst (copper).

3 See text.

4 Speeds up rate (the positive Fe^{2+} ions attract the negatively charged $S_2O_8^{2-}$ ions) – the negatively charged $S_2O_8^{2-}$ and I^- ions repel each other.
   The Fe^{2+} ions are regenerated and are therefore chemically unchanged.

Chemical equilibrium

1 a The equilibrium will shift to the left, favouring the reverse reaction.

   b The equilibrium will shift to the right, favouring the forward reaction.

   c The equilibrium will shift to the left, favouring the reverse reaction.

   d No effect.

2 The **forward** reaction is exothermic. Increasing the temperature favours the endothermic reaction, which is the reverse reaction, forming more $NO_2(g)$.

3 The forward reaction is endothermic and favoured by an increase in temperature. Therefore the higher the temperature the better for formation of *Syngas*. However this means more energy used. $850\,°C$ is a compromise.
   The forward reaction is favoured by a lowering of pressure since more gas molecules are on the right-hand side of the equilibrium. A lowering of pressure would reduce the rate, because it effectively lowers the concentration of gases.
   The pressure used is a compromise between a good yield (low pressure) and a fast rate (high pressure).

Module 4 – Resources

The greenhouse effect and global warming

1 a See text.

   b Much higher concentration in the atmosphere.

2 a See text.

   b See text.

3 See text.

Atmospheric pollution

1 a $Cl\cdot$ radicals

   b NO_x/oxides of nitrogen. The high temperatures of jet exhausts and thunderstorms are necessary to break the very strong $N\equiv N$ bond.

2 a See text

   b See text

   c They speed up the breakdown of ozone and are regenerated.

3 HFCs contain fluorine only.
   Only bonds present are C–F and C–H bonds.
   These are not broken by UV light – too strong.
   Do not produce radicals.
   CFCs contain chlorine and hence C—Cl bonds that can be broken by UV light.
   To produce $Cl\cdot$ radicals that will breakdown ozone layer.

4 They have to form bonds with reactants that are strong enough for them to adsorb to surface.
   They also have to form bonds that are strong enough for the bonds in the reactants to break, and for reaction to occur.
   The bonds with the products have to be weak enough for these to be able to desorb from the surface.

5 See text.

6 a See text.

   b See text.

   c See text.

Green chemistry and sustainability

1 a 44.1%

   b 100%

2 36%

3 See text.

4 See text.

5 See text.

Answers to end-of-unit questions

Unit 1 Atoms, bonds and groups

1 **a** **i** 14; **ii** 10; **iii** 8; **iv** 4 (4)
   b **i** 2 mol Ca^{2+} 4 mol Cl^-; **ii** +5; **iii** 32 (3)
   c **i** 69.80; **ii** 3 g; **iii** 4 g (3)

2 **a** **i** $CaF_2 + H_2SO_4 \rightarrow 2HF + CaSO_4$ (1)
      ii Amount (in mol) of $CaF_2 = 7.81/78.1 = 0.1$ mol. (1)
         Amount (in mol) of $HF = 0.2$ mol; volume of gas $= 0.2 \times 24\,dm^3 = 4.8\,dm^3$ (1)
   b **i** I   II (4)

      ii Any two (1 mark each) of: (2)
         HF is a gas, CaF_2 is a solid
         or
         HF has low melting and boiling points; CaF_2 has high melting and boiling points.
         HF does not conduct electricity as a liquid or as a gas; CaF_2 conducts electricity as a liquid or in solution, but not in solid form.
         HF is simple molecular/consists of discrete molecules; CaF_2 is a giant ionic substance/structure is giant ionic lattice.
   c **i** (2)

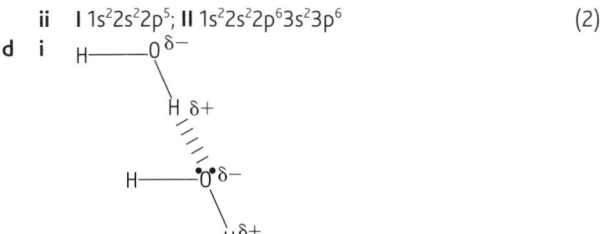

      ii I $1s^2 2s^2 2p^5$; II $1s^2 2s^2 2p^6 3s^2 3p^6$ (2)
   d **i**

$$H\!-\!\!O^{\delta-}$$
$$H^{\delta+}$$
$$H\!-\!\!O^{\delta-}$$
$$H^{\delta+}$$

         (1) for correct dipoles; (1) for lone-pair electrons; (1) for dashed bond between $\delta+$ and $\delta-$ (3)
      ii Hydrogen bonding between water molecules is stronger than the van der Waals' forces/instantaneous dipoles between methane molecules. (2)
   e Both produce H^+ ions/both are proton (H^+) donors. (1)
   f **i** $CaCO_3 + 2HF \rightarrow CaF_2 + CO_2 + H_2O$. (1)
      ii Fizzing/effervescence; CO_2 gas is produced. (1)

3 **a** +4 in SO_2; +6 in SO_4^{2-} (2)
   b The sulfur is oxidised; oxidation number increases from +4 to +6. (1)
      The iodine is reduced; oxidation number decreases from 0 to –1. (1)
   c **i** 0.000164 mol; **ii** 0.000164 mol. (2)
      iii 0.0032 mol dm^{-3}. (1)
      iv M of $SO_2 = 64.1$ g dm^{-3}; 0.210 g dm^{-3}. (2)

4 **a** The energy required to remove one electron from each atom (1)
      in 1 mole of gaseous atoms (1)
      to form 1 mole of gaseous +1 ions. (1)
   b When plotted against atomic number, it shows a repeating pattern (in each period). (1)

c The overall trend is a general increase across the period. (1)
   Increasing nuclear charge attracts the electrons more strongly, therefore making it difficult to remove an electron. (1)
d The atomic radius and distance from nucleus and electron shielding both increase; (1)
   therefore less attraction on outer electron. (1)
e See text page 18.

Unit 2 Chains, energy and resources

1 **a** **i** Alkenes. (1)
      ii A and D (2)
   b **i** C (1)
      ii Heat with concentrated sulfuric/concentrated phosphoric acid. (2)

2

Alcohol	Observation	Organic product (if any)
butan-1-ol	orange to green	butanal or butanoic acid
butan-2-ol	orange to green	butan-2-one
2-methylpropan-2-ol	no change (stays orange)	no reaction

(6)

3 **a**

$$\left[\begin{array}{cc} H & Cl \\ | & | \\ C & C \\ | & | \\ H & H \end{array}\right]_n$$

(1)
   b It is non-biodegradable and will persist in the environment. If it is burned, it will give toxic products. (2)

4 **a** Addition of one molecule to another, to form one molecule only.
      Example: the reaction of bromine with an alkene.
      The reactants are added together at room temperature in the dark.
      $Br_2 + C_2H_4 \rightarrow C_2H_4Br_2$ (4)
   b Removal of a small molecule such as H_2O from a molecule.
      Example: elimination of H_2O from ethanol to give ethene.
      The ethanol is heated with a concentrated solution of acid.
      $CH_3CH_2OH \rightarrow C_2H_4 + H_2O$ (4)
   c A halogen atom is replaced by another group or atom.
      Example: substitution of Br in bromoethane by OH to give ethanol.
      The bromoethane is refluxed with an aqueous solution of KOH. (4)
      $CH_3CH_2Br + KOH \rightarrow CH_3CH_2OH + KBr$

5 a **E** is an alkane because its formula fits the general formula for alkanes (C_nH_{2n+2}).
It is hexane.
The unsaturated hydrocarbon, **G**, is an alkene, and its molecular mass corresponds to propene, C_3H_6.
($3 \times 12 + 6 = 42$).
Therefore **F** is propane (C_3H_8)
$C_6H_{14} \rightarrow C_3H_8 + C_3H_6$.
In the presence of UV light, **E** would undergo substitution to give **H**, $C_6H_{15}Br$, bromohexane, and HBr – the acidic gas **I**.
$C_6H_{14} + Br_2 \rightarrow C_6H_{13}Br + HBr$
G, propene, reacts with HBr to give two products, 1-bromopropane and 2-bromopropane.
$C_3H_6 + HBr \rightarrow C_3H_7Br$ (10)

b Because straight-chain compounds produce knocking when they burn. Benzene and cyclohexane. (3)

c 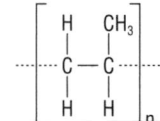 (1)

6 a i Compounds with the same molecular formula but with different structural formulae. (1)
ii Any alkane with 6–10 carbons, e.g. C_8H_{18}. (1)
b i UV radiation. (2)
ii C_4H_9Cl.*The chlorine accounts for 35.5 of the molecular mass, leaving 57 for C_4H_9. (2)
iii Either of the following. (2)

H—C—C—C—C—Cl   H—C—C—C—C—H

1-chlorobutane   2-chlorobutane

7 a **i, ii** Student's sketch (see text). (3)
b **i, ii** Student's sketch (see text).
iii At the higher temperature, more molecules can react because more molecules exceed the activation energy, therefore the rate of reaction increases. (7)

8 a Enthalpy change of complete combustion of 1 mole of methane gas under standard conditions (298 K, 101 kPa). (3)
b i $\Delta H^{\ominus}_f = -393.5 + 2(-285.9) - (-890.3)$
= $-75\,kJ\,mol^{-1}$ (2)
ii Practical difficulty of reacting carbon with hydrogen – the reaction has a high activation energy and produces a mixture of hydrocarbons. (2)
c $3000\,dm^3 \times 60\% = 1800\,dm^3$.
$1800\,dm^3 = 75\,mol\,CH_4$
heat energy produced = $75 \times (-890.3)$
$= -6.677\,kJ\,mol^{-1}$. (3)

9 a $N_2(g) + 3H_2(g) \rightleftharpoons 2NH_3(g)$ (1)
b i 100 kPa; 298 K; $1\,mol\,dm^{-3}$ (3)
ii High pressure favours the forward reaction because fewer gas molecules are formed and this would lower the pressure. The high pressure increases the concentration of the gases speeding up the reaction. The forward reaction is favoured by a lowering of temperature. However, this would make the reaction rate too low. 450°C is a moderately high temperature. This would favour the reverse reaction but would still allow a reasonable yield. The catalyst lowers the activation energy, speeding up the rate, and saves energy, and can be used again and again. (12)
c A catalyst speeds up a chemical reaction, by allowing the reaction to proceed by a different route, with a lower activation energy. (3)
d

N_2	+	$3H_2$	$\rightleftharpoons$	$2NH_3$
$N\equiv N$		3H–H		6N–H
945		3×436		6×391
+2252				−2346

$\Delta H_r^{\ominus} = -93\,kJ\,mol^{-1}$ (3)

10 a i O_3 (1)
ii The reaction $O_3(g) \rightarrow O_2(g) + O(g)$ absorbs ultraviolet radiation and stops UV getting to the Earth's surface. (3)
b It is exothermic, increasing the temperature. (2)
c Ultraviolet radiation can reach the Earth's surface, damaging living creatures/causing skin cancer/disrupting plant metabolism. (2)
d $NO• + O_3 \rightarrow NO_2• + O_2$
$NO_2• + O \rightarrow NO• + O_2$ (4)
e i Better overall yield and atom economy, fewer unwanted products formed. (2)
ii $50 \times 50 \times 50/100 \times 100 \times 100 = 12.5\%$ (2)

Index

Module 3 – Energy

Enthalpy changes

1. a Exothermic
    b —
    c The chemical system has lost heat energy to the surroundings, therefore enthalpy change **for the system** is negative.

2.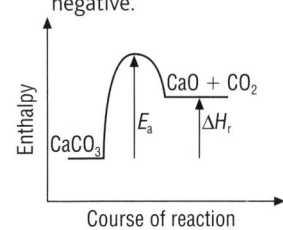

3. a see text   b see text

4.

Compound	Equation to represent $\Delta H_f^{\ominus}$	Equation to represent $\Delta H_c^{\ominus}$
$C_2H_6(g)$	$2C(s) + 3H_2(g)$ $\rightarrow C_2H_6(g)$	$C_2H_6(g) + 3\frac{1}{2} O_2$ $\rightarrow 2CO_2(g) + 3H_2O(l)$
$CO(g)$	$C(s) + \frac{1}{2} O_2(g)$ $\rightarrow CO(g)$	$CO(g) + \frac{1}{2} O_2(g)$ $\rightarrow CO_2(g)$
$CH_3OH(l)$	$C(s) + 2H_2(g) + \frac{1}{2} O_2(g)$ $\rightarrow CH_3OH(l)$	$CH_3OH(l) + 1\frac{1}{2} O_2(g)$ $\rightarrow CO_2(g) + 2H_2O(l)$
$N_2H_4(l)$	$N_2(g) + 2H_2(g)$ $\rightarrow N_2H_4(l)$	$N_2H_4(l) + O_2(g)$ $\rightarrow N_2(g) + 2H_2O(l)$

5. $1173/3 = 391$ kJ mol^{-1}

Calculating enthalpy changes

1. a -1318 kJ mol^{-1} b -212 kJ mol^{-1}
2. a -623 kJ mol^{-1} b $+155$ kJ mol^{-1}
3. a $Zn(s) + CuSO_4(aq) \rightarrow Cu(s) + ZnSO_4(aq)$
    b 10605 J $= 10.6$ kJ
    c -10605 J$/0.05 = -212$ kJ mol^{-1}

Reaction rates

1.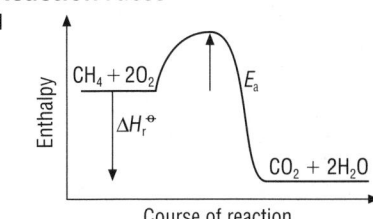

2. a Increasing surface area of the zinc/using zinc powder/using smaller pieces of zinc.
       Increasing the temperature/warming the acid.
       Increasing the concentration of the sulfuric acid solution
       Adding a catalyst (copper).
3. See text.
4. Speeds up rate (the positive Fe^{2+} ions attract the negatively charged $S_2O_8^{2-}$ ions) – the negatively charged $S_2O_8^{2-}$ and I^- ions repel each other.
    The Fe^{2+} ions are regenerated and are therefore chemically unchanged.

Chemical equilibrium

1. a The equilibrium will shift to the left, favouring the reverse reaction.
    b The equilibrium will shift to the right, favouring the forward reaction.
    c The equilibrium will shift to the left, favouring the reverse reaction.
    d No effect.
2. The **forward** reaction is exothermic. Increasing the temperature favours the endothermic reaction, which is the reverse reaction, forming more $NO_2(g)$.
3. The forward reaction is endothermic and favoured by an increase in temperature. Therefore the higher the temperature the better for formation of *Syngas*. However this means more energy used. 850 °C is a compromise.
    The forward reaction is favoured by a lowering of pressure since more gas molecules are on the right-hand side of the equilibrium. A lowering of pressure would reduce the rate, because it effectively lowers the concentration of gases.
    The pressure used is a compromise between a good yield (low pressure) and a fast rate (high pressure).

Module 4 – Resources

The greenhouse effect and global warming

1. a See text.
    b Much higher concentration in the atmosphere.
2. a See text.
    b See text.
3. See text.

Atmospheric pollution

1. a $Cl\bullet$ radicals
    b NO_x/oxides of nitrogen. The high temperatures of jet exhausts and thunderstorms are necessary to break the very strong $N\equiv N$ bond.
2. a See text
    b See text
    c They speed up the breakdown of ozone and are regenerated.
3. HFCs contain fluorine only.
    Only bonds present are C–F and C–H bonds.
    These are not broken by UV light – too strong.
    Do not produce radicals.
    CFCs contain chlorine and hence C—Cl bonds that can be broken by UV light.
    To produce $Cl\bullet$ radicals that will breakdown ozone layer.
4. They have to form bonds with reactants that are strong enough for them to adsorb to surface.
    They also have to form bonds that are strong enough for the bonds in the reactants to break, and for reaction to occur.
    The bonds with the products have to be weak enough for these to be able to desorb from the surface.
5. See text.
6. a See text.
    b See text.
    c See text.

Green chemistry and sustainability

1. a 44.1%
    b 100%
2. 36%
3. See text.
4. See text.
5. See text.

b i   **ii**

iii   **iv**

2 a Carbon monoxide
   b Carbon monoxide, hydrogen chloride and polychlorinated biphenyls

3 a

   b Carbon monoxide, oxides of nitrogen (NO_x) or more specifically nitrogen dioxide, hydrogen cyanide.

Module 2 – Alcohols, halogenoalkanes and analysis

The alcohols

1 a i propan-1-ol $CH_3CH_2CH_2OH$;
        propan-2-ol $CH_3CH(OH)CH_3$
    ii butan-1-ol $CH_3CH_2CH_2CH_2OH$;
        butan-2-ol $CH_3CH(OH)CH_2CH_3$
        2-methylpropan-1-ol $(CH_3)_2CHCH_2OH$
        2-methylpropan-2-ol $(CH_3)_3COH$
   b 3-methylbutan-1-ol
2 a i See text
    ii The oxygen in the O–H bond is more electronegative than the hydrogen in this bond, so the electron density on the oxygen is greater.
    iii See text
3 a $C_3H_7OH + 4\frac{1}{2} O_2 \rightarrow 3CO_2 + 4H_2O$
   b They can be produced from plant sources – sugar for ethanol; wood for methanol.
4 a propene $CH_3CH=CH_2$
   b but-1-ene $CH_3CH_2CH=CH_2$;
      but-2-ene (E and Z) $CH_3CH=CHCH_3$
5 a $CH_3CH_2OH + CH_3COOH \rightarrow CH_3COOCH_2CH_3 + H_2O$
   b $CH_3CH_2CH_2OH + HCOOH \rightarrow HCOOCH_2CH_2CH_3 + H_2O$
   c $CH_3OH + CH_3COOH \rightarrow CH_3COOCH_3 + H_2O$

Types of alcohol

1 a primary   **b** secondary
   c primary   **d** tertiary
   e secondary
2 The ethanol is oxidised to ethanoic acid.
3 Use acidified potassium dichromate(VI) and heat.
The 2-methylpropan-2-ol will have no effect, because it is a tertiary alcohol, and therefore the acidified potassium dichromate stays orange. The butan-2-ol will cause the orange colour to change to greeny-blue because it is oxidised to a ketone, butan-2-one.
4 When the alcohol concentration reaches 15% the yeast is killed and the reaction stops.

The halogenoalkanes

1 a C_3H_7Br
   b C_3H_7Br
   c

2 The isomers are:

$CH_3CH_2CH_2CH_2Br$	1-bromobutane
$CH_3CHBrCH_2CH_3$	2-bromobutane
$CH_3CBr(CH_3)CH_3$	2-bromo-2-methylpropane
$CH_3CH(CH_3)CH_2Br$	1-bromo-2-methylpropane

3 a The synthesis relies on the halogen being replaced by another group and therefore the breaking of the carbon–halogen bond. The C–F bond is very strong and therefore difficult to break, so the reaction would be extremely slow and not viable as part of a synthetic route.
   b The C–I bond is too weak and consequently iodoalkanes often react with contaminants before they can be used in a reaction. Bromoalkanes are sufficiently reactive to make them useful in syntheses, but not so reactive that they are unstable or react too easily.

Reactions of the halogenoalkanes

1 The OH⁻ ion is negative and is therefore attracted to the electron-deficient carbon in the carbon–halogen bond and has a lone pair of electrons which it can donate to the carbon during the reaction.
2 a $CH_2BrCH_2Br + 2KOH \rightarrow 2KBr + CH_2OHCH_2OH$
    can have $CH_2BrCH_2Br + KOH \rightarrow KBr + CH_2BrCH_2OH$
    or $CH_2BrCH_2Br + KOH \rightarrow KBr + CH_2(OH)CH_2Br$
3 Comparable halogenoalkanes such as 1-bromobutane and 1-chlorobutane (both with 4 carbons and both primary halogenoalkanes) are used to make it a fair test.
Silver nitrate solution is dissolved in alcohol and the solution warmed gently (50°C) in two separate test tubes.
Equal amounts of the 1-bromobutane and 1-chlorobutane are added separately to each tube. The appearance of a precipitate indicates the formation of insoluble silver halide.
The speed of the appearance of the precipitate indicates the ease of breaking of the carbon–halogen bond – it is quicker for the 1-bromobutane, indicating that the carbon–bromine bond is the weaker of the two.
4 a Easily vaporized/low boiling point and non-corrosive.
   b Unreactive and heavy vapours, so will not burn, and sink onto fire, excluding oxygen.
   c Good solvents for grease/oil also will evaporate easily so dry quickly.

Infrared spectroscopy

1 a –OH group
   b alcohol
2 At first the absorption due to the –OH group (at ~ 3400 cm⁻¹ the alcohol will disappear as this is oxidised to a carbonyl (C=O) group in the aldehyde. At the same time the absorption at ~1700 cm⁻¹ appears and gets stronger.
As the aldehyde is then oxidised to a carboxylic acid a broad absorption at 2500–3300 cm⁻¹ appears. The absorption due to the carbonyl group remains.
3 The ethoxyethane has no –OH group and therefore there will be no absorption at ~3400 cm⁻¹.
4 The propan-2-ol will not absorb at ~1700 cm⁻¹ because it has no carbonyl (C=O) group.

Mass spectrometry

1 72
2

Peak m/e	Ion responsible	Equation for formation of ion
15	CH_3^+	$CH_3CH_2OH^+ \rightarrow CH_3^+ + \bullet CH_2OH$
29	$CH_3CH_2^+$	$CH_3CH_2OH^+ \rightarrow CH_3CH_2^+ + \bullet OH$
31	CH_2OH^+	$CH_3CH_2OH^+ \rightarrow CH_2OH^+ + \bullet CH_3$